THE GREE

Rose Elliot began cooking a[...] family's vegetarian retreat centre in Hampshire. Her first book, *Simply Delicious*, followed soon after in 1967 and was an immediate success. Rose has been at the forefront of the vegetarian movement ever since, and has written over two dozen best-selling vegetarian cookery books, including *Not Just a Load of Old Lentils*, *The Bean Book* and the acclaimed *Vegetarian Cookery*.

A vegetarian since the age of three, Rose's first challenge was to show that vegetarian food could be as delicious and attractive as conventional meat dishes. Lately, whilst still being passionately enthusiastic about the quality of vegetarian cooking, Rose has become increasingly interested in the global, health and ecological issues involved in food production, and this has led to the writing of this book.

Rose is married with three daughters. Her other main interest is astrology, which she practises professionally; with her husband, she runs a computer astrology service, Rose Elliot Horoscopes.

There is a single magic, a single power,
a single salvation and a single happiness,
and that is called loving.

HERMANN HESSE

CONTENTS

Contents

ACKNOWLEDGEMENTS

I would particularly like to express my gratitude to Carole Hamlin for providing, after a fated 'chance' meeting, the initial inspiration which led to the writing of this book. I am also greatly indebted to John Robbins and his superb book, *Diet for a New America*, surely a blueprint for a Green Age which is destined to become a classic, and a rich source of inspiration and facts. The works of Dr Michael Klaper, George Eismann and Dr John McDougall have also been especially helpful. I would like to thank my friends and family, especially my husband Anthony, and my daughter Margaret, and my agent Barbara Levy, for their support and encouragement over this book and for their most helpful comments on the manuscript, and also my editor, Kelly Davis, for her work and her many excellent suggestions; and Michael Fishwick and Simon King of Fontana for making it happen.

INTRODUCTION: BEST FOR US, BEST FOR THE WORLD

I started writing this book simply in response to my publisher's and many readers' requests for a book on slimming. However, as I progressed, many facts which had been dimly in the back of my mind started to come into sharp focus – facts about our bodies and the enormous importance, both for ourselves and the environment, of what we choose to eat. Thus, my slimming book turned into *The Green Age Diet* and my initial interest in the subject became a passionate belief in a new approach to food.

The first thing I realized was how many physiological characteristics we share with herbivorous animals and how little we have in common with carnivores. A lion or tiger, for instance, has a hinged jaw and can only chew with an up and down motion; a horse, like us, has a sliding jaw so that he can chew in a rotary motion and grind up grains. The teeth of a true carnivore are long, overlapping fangs, while a herbivore has flat, grinding molars, like ours. A carnivore laps when it drinks, a herbivore sucks; a carnivore has retractable claws; a herbivore does not.

The saliva and digestive juices in the stomach of a carnivore are extremely acid in order to digest animal flesh. The saliva and digestive juices of a herbivore are much less acid, as are ours. Again, a true carnivore has a short, smooth intestine, to get rid of meat quickly, while a herbivore has a long intestine with a bumpy, ridged inner surface to digest grains, grasses, leaves and vegetables slowly. A horse, for instance, has an intestine which is six or eight times the length of its body, and our intestine is even longer. In proportion to our size, it is half as long again as that of a horse.

A carnivore has a natural instinct to kill for meat and then to eat it raw, whereas herbivores lack this urge. Loving and caring for animals comes naturally to most people and maltreating or killing animals is abhorrent to them.

Having looked at the physiology of the body, I then studied the results of research on the effects of feeding herbivorous animals with a carnivorous diet. Because a herbivore's liver was not made to get rid of large amounts of cholesterol quickly, the cholesterol gums up the arteries and heart, eventually blocking them. Also, because a herbivore's intestine was designed to digest grains slowly, meat stays in the gut too long, and produces carcinogenic substances which trigger cancers. In other words, we are literally giving ourselves coronary disease and cancer by eating a diet for which our body simply was not designed. If you fed a pet on a diet as unsuitable for its type, you would probably be accused of cruelty.

Looking further afield, I realized that not only are we destroying our bodies by feeding them the wrong food, we are also destroying the environment. Because it takes about 16 kg of vegetable protein to make 1 kg of meat, farmers have been using more and more chemicals on the land in the struggle to produce enough animal feed. Eighty per cent of the crops grown in Britain and America are fed to animals, and that still isn't enough. Extra crops are being imported from the starving Third World to fatten animals for meat in the West. Huge areas of rainforest are being destroyed each year to provide grazing land for cows to make hamburgers. And those hamburgers are damaging our health. It doesn't make sense.

But, turn all this on its head and eat more grains, fruits and vegetables direct from the land instead of passing them through animals first, and it would become possible to grow more of our food organically. If we stopped eating so many animal products, there wouldn't be such need to import crops from the Third World, or to cut down any more rainforest for the purpose of producing cheap beef. The pressure on our farmland would be considerably relieved, our rivers and streams would become free of nitrates and chemicals from agricultural run-off. People eating such a diet would become lean, fit and well, because it's the right diet for their type of body. Heart disease, circulatory diseases, cancer and all the suffering which these involve would decrease, and maybe even become a thing of the past. Hundreds of millions of pounds would be saved every year on medical care ...

What is so exciting about this is that individual people like us can actually make it happen. It is not up to 'them' in government. It is about the choices which you and I make in the shop, in the supermarket, in the kitchen, every mealtime, every day. That is where the power lies. What we buy, cook and eat could not only save our health, but the earth itself.

PART ONE

All About the Green Age Diet

1

What is Happening Now

Today, 500 million people in the world are, according to Oxfam figures, severely undernourished. Forty thousand children starve to death every single day — that's one every two seconds. Water is becoming so badly polluted that experts are increasingly concerned about future supplies. And huge areas of the great rainforests of South America, with their incredibly rich and varied plant and animal life, are being cut down every year, with deeply damaging effects on the world's climate.

Our agricultural practices are also destroying the environment. Constant use of chemical fertilizers is causing serious soil erosion and these, as well as pesticides, are poisoning the land, the rivers, the animals and man himself.

Soil needs humus — decaying animal and vegetable matter such as manure, grass stubble and compost — to put back into it important minerals and also to hold it together. One of the major problems of modern farming with artificial fertilizers is that there is no humus. So fields and prairies can quickly turn into dustbowls.

In traditional farming, the farmer nurtured the soil and made sure that the nutrients were returned to it in plant matter, compost and animal manure. He grew some crops specially to put back certain nutrients into the soil compost and animal manure, and he rotated crops so that one type of pest or disease did not have a chance to build up. Using these methods, he did not need artificial fertilizers, pesticides or herbicides. But in modern, intensive farming, more and more nitrate

3

fertilizers, pesticides and sprays are needed to produce crops.

The chemicals used as pesticides and herbicides are among the most poisonous known to man. For instance 2,4-D and 2,4,5-T, which are used as herbicides, are the two active ingredients in Agent Orange, which was used to destroy so much plant life in the Vietnam War. Animals have contracted cancer in tests using 2,4-D; and 2,4,5-T contains dioxin which, in laboratory experiments, causes cancer, miscarriages and birth defects.

Governments are often slow to ban pesticides, and even when they do, their effects last for many years because they do not break down easily. For example, dieldrin was banned in the USA in 1974, but by then it was found in 96 per cent of all meat, fish and poultry in the United States, in 85 per cent of all dairy produce, and in 99.5 per cent of the flesh of American people. And even as late as 1980 it was still being found in turkey products in 'intolerable levels'. Although dieldrin is no longer applied to soils, it remains *in* the soil. Dieldrin is one of the most potent carcinogens ever known: it causes cancer in animals at every dosage tested, including the most infinitesimal amounts. In the UK it has been banned from all agricultural use for over ten years but is still present in rivers, making many fish, particularly eels, unfit to eat.

Of course this problem of pesticides is not restricted to meat and animal products. It applies to fruit, vegetables and grains, as well as to animal feed. However, when these poisons are eaten via an animal product, they are more concentrated. Meat contains approximately 14 times more pesticides than plant foods; dairy foods 5.5 times more. This is because an animal has to eat perhaps 16 kg of grain in order to produce 1 kg of meat. So any poison in the grain is intensified, and animals store the pesticides in their bodies. Furthermore, grains produced for animal feed are sprayed more heavily than those grown for humans.

And pesticides are not the only chemicals found in meat. Even before the animal is born the mother will probably have been given drugs throughout her pregnancy and to induce the birth. Then, from birth until slaughter, the animal will be given regular doses of antibiotics and other drugs.

Artificial hormone 'growth promoters' are now officially banned in the EEC and supposedly strictly controlled in the USA. However it's difficult to test for the drugs, inspection is inadequate, loopholes abound and supplies can be obtained on the black market. So the situation is far from satisfactory.

The long-term effects of eating regular doses of growth hormones are extremely worrying. In Puerto Rico, where their use is not strictly regulated, it is not uncommon to find sexually mature four- and five-year-olds and even babies as young as one year old with fully developed breasts and menstrual periods, as well as boys with swollen breasts. When these children stop eating meat and milk their symptoms usually lessen.

The situation in Europe and the USA is not as severe. However children are certainly reaching puberty earlier and there are more reported cases of sexual abnormalities in adults. These are usually put down to 'an imbalance in the patient's endocrine system'. But a more likely reason is that they are taking regular doses of sex hormones in their meat and milk, especially when the symptoms disappear once they stop eating these foods!

Whether or not hormones are used in meat production, antibiotics almost certainly are, in order to ensure the animals' survival in the conditions under which they are reared. These antibiotics are passed on to humans in meat and milk. You may not mind taking a daily dose of antibiotics, but one of the problems is that when antibiotics are used regularly, by either animals or humans, the bugs become resistant to them. So when antibiotics are needed to treat an infection, they don't work. This is one of the reasons why salmonella poisoning is becoming such a problem.

Salmonella is a bacterium found in meat and eggs. It is spread by the faeces of infected animals getting into the meat.

They can also get into the oviducts of hens and from there into eggs. This can easily happen when animals or birds are reared intensively because they are crowded together and get smeared with their own faeces and those of other animals. It also happens when they are slaughtered; if the gut is ruptured and the faeces contain salmonella bacteria, they can easily get into the meat.

Because the salmonella bacteria are becoming more and more resistant to antibiotics, it is more difficult to keep down infection among animals and to treat it in humans. According to the *Farmers' Weekly*, 'Britain is sitting on a salmonella time-bomb' and the situation is equally serious in Europe and the USA.

It was estimated that in the late 1980s at least 35 per cent of all factory farm chickens sold in Britain, Europe and America were contaminated with salmonella. The level of contamination reached 70 per cent in some cities. In New York City, one type of food-poisoning bacterium or another was found in 52 per cent of roast beef, 53 per cent of chicken breast, and 17 per cent of ground beef.

Infected meat or eggs can cause food poisoning in humans if they are not cooked for long enough or if they do not reach a high enough temperature to kill the bugs. This can also happen if infected raw meat or egg touches any other food or equipment in the kitchen. Salmonella spreads very easily.

The symptoms of salmonella poisoning are sickness, diarrhoea, stomach cramps and a raised temperature. At best it is very unpleasant and at worst it can be fatal in those who are already weak or sick, in babies and the elderly.

The dangers of intensive farming practices are again illustrated very clearly by the recent development of a disease in cattle called Bovine Spongiform Encephalopathy (BSE). For a number of years sheep have been known to be infected by a disease called scrapie. This was thought to be confined to sheep. However the brain and offal of sheep are made into feed which is given to cattle. The result of this is that cattle have developed a variant of the disease called BSE. This turns their brains into sponges, full of little holes, makes them behave aggressively, fall about and then die. There is now a strong possibility that this disease or a variant of it will be passed on to humans through the meat or dairy industries. This is a situation which is causing considerable concern to many people.

So meat is produced from animals reared on foodstuffs grown with high levels of nitrates from artificial fertilizers or produced from the carcases of other, possibly diseased, animals. These foodstuffs have also been sprayed with poisonous herbicides, insecticides and fungicides. The animals are then continuously dosed with antibiotics and other chemicals, perhaps including artificial hormones. And they may be infected with salmonella bacteria or other diseases such as BSE.

As a finishing touch, before it is sold, meat may be coloured with artificial colourings, dosed with monosodium glutamate (MSG), preserved with nitrates or sulphur dioxide, or doctored with nitrogen, carbon dioxide, oxygen or carbon monoxide to improve the colouring. When you think about all these 'hidden extras', eating meat starts to sound like quite a risk.

2

Towards a Green Future

In recent years the organic movement has been gaining strength, to the point where several major supermarkets now stock organic produce and a number of farmers are considering changing to organic methods. Although organic farming produces a lower yield – 10 to 20 per cent less – than farming with artificial chemicals, there are substantial savings on chemicals, oil and petrol. In fact a survey in Switzerland showed that the net income for organic farms was the same as for comparable farms using chemical sprays and fertilizers.

The transition from inorganic to organic farming may take four to five years, as 'good heart' is put back into the soil. But an increasing number of farmers are showing that it can be done. They also say that they and their workers find organic farming more satisfying. But if organic farming were adopted on a large scale, what would the 10 to 20 per cent drop in production mean in a world which is short of food?

Firstly the developed countries would have to reduce their consumption of meat and animal products. As we have seen, it takes 16 kg of grain and soya protein to produce 1 kg of beef. In addition, it takes 11,250 litres (2500 gallons) of water – as much water as a typical family uses for all purposes in a month – to produce 450 g (1 lb) of beef.

While it is processing the grain and soya protein, one cow produces as much waste each day as 16 humans. In fact it has been estimated that the livestock population of the UK and USA produce 20 times as much excrement as the entire human population of those countries! Instead of going back on to the land to replace valuable nitrogen, as it always used to, this waste gets pumped away and pollutes the rivers with harmful nitrates and ammonia and the atmosphere with methane. The meat industry accounts for three times as much dangerous organic waste as all other industries combined.

In Britain and America, more than half the harvested land is used to grow feed for animals, and the figure rises to over 90 per cent if you include grazing land. Yet we still do not have enough to feed all our livestock and have to import more. About 60 per cent of this extra feed comes from the malnourished Third World. So they are growing food for our animals to produce meat instead of growing food for themselves, when large sections of their populations are starving to death. Worldwide, over 450 million tonnes – more than a third of the food grains produced – are fed to livestock. It can take enough grain to support an African family for a whole week to produce one large steak.

In Brazil, at the time of writing, areas of rainforest the size of Wales are being cut down each year to make grazing land for animals supplying the fast-food hamburger market in the West. This land is totally unsuited for the purpose because most of the nutrients are in the plants which grow above the ground, and when they are taken away, the nutrients go with them. Because there are no trees, the soil is exposed to scorching sun and torrential rainfall, resulting in severe erosion. The 'reclaimed' land has a useful life of just a few years before it becomes so unproductive that it has to be abandoned as virtual desert.

Yet this need not be so. Instead of relying heavily on imports, as it does at present, Britain could feed roughly five times its population on a pure vegetarian diet. And the same is true of America. To make a detailed comparison, it takes about 1¾ acres of land to feed one meat-eater for one year; ½ acre of land to feed one lacto-vegetarian for one year; and ⅙ acre of land to feed one pure vegetarian for one year. So a given area of land can supply food for one meat-eater or about twenty pure vegetarians.

In addition, intensive production of meat uses a massive amount of energy in heating, removing animal waste and transporting animals and feed. Far less energy is needed to produce vegetarian food. It has been estimated that the least efficient vegetable protein requires ten times less fuel than the most efficiently produced animal protein. And it takes less water to produce a year's food for a pure vegetarian than to produce a month's food for a meat-eater.

It seems that we could easily produce enough food for the whole world if we ate it directly instead of processing it through animals first. Writing about a vegetarian agriculture in the UK, Professor Watkin Williams, from the Department of Agricultural Botany at the University of Reading, had this to say:

> National food requirements based only on crop production could be provided from half of the present yield per acre — the yield level in the early part of this century when no artificial nitrogen was applied. In this way 500,000 tonnes of elemental nitrogen and 1,000,000 litres of oil would be saved.

In a mainly vegetarian world, there would be some animals on grazing land and there would be conservation areas; there would also be more upland forests, reducing our need for artificial energy sources. Finally, there would be enough food to go round and pollution would be greatly reduced.

3

Healthier Eating

As we have seen, the food we choose to eat has far-reaching effects on the lives of others, the land and world ecology. The interesting thing is that changing our eating habits to benefit the environment will also benefit us. Cut down on eating animal flesh and fats, or stop eating them altogether, and your health will improve dramatically and any extra pounds will drop off.

As our bodies have so many herbivorous characteristics, it seems only natural for us to follow a herbivorous diet. But what do herbivores eat? A herbivorous diet contains lots of fibre, lots of carbohydrates, not much protein and little or no fat. The human body works beautifully on a herbivorous diet. In the past, every major civilization has had a grain as its staple food; now the United States and Europe and the Eskimos don't.

A carnivorous diet contains the exact opposite of the herbivore's diet: lots of fat, lots of protein and little fibre or carbohydrate. If you fill a car with the wrong fuel it will not run well and will eventually seize up. It's the same if you constantly feed a body with the wrong fuel. Too much fat, too much protein and too little fibre spells trouble as far as the human body is concerned.

Too Much Animal Fat

All calories were not created equal. Protein, carbohydrates and fats all contain calories, but they have vastly different effects on the body.

The body of a herbivore is designed to burn carbohydrates, and to store fats. And all animal flesh, however lean, contains fat. After you eat a hamburger the fatty serum floats through your bloodstream. As it passes your fat stores they gather it up and store it away.

If you don't eat animal fat, you burn off your fat stores rather than adding to them. You also stop craving sweets. This is because some brain cells can only run on sugar, and so after a large meal with lots of fat and protein they still need sugar. If you eat a meal of starchy foods, your body can rapidly turn these into sugars and your brain cells get what they need. That craving for sweet things just disappears.

In addition, meals based on unrefined carbohydrates will satisfy you for longer. Being higher in natural fibre, they are digested slowly, keeping your blood sugar levels more even. So you don't get that sudden drop in blood sugar which makes it difficult to resist snacks. For all these reasons, as soon as you stop eating meat and animal fat, the pounds begin to drop off and you become lean, fit and healthy.

Obesity is a serious modern problem caused by running a herbivorous body on the wrong fuel. But there are other even more serious problems. When we eat foods which contain animal fat, the fatty serum moves through our bloodstream and some of it sticks to the insides of the arteries. If we go on eating like this, the fatty deposits build up year after year so that the channels in the arteries become smaller and smaller and eventually clog up. This is called atherosclerosis.

If this happens to the blood vessels inside your heart the heart muscle is deprived of oxygen and you get terrible crushing pains called angina pectoris. Because of the damage to the arteries they may start bleeding through the fatty deposits and form blood clots. When one of the arteries supplying blood to the heart gets completely closed up or blocked by a breakaway clot from an artery elsewhere in the body, the result is a heart attack.

Every year one million Americans and 300,000 Britons die of cardiovascular disease, amounting to one-third of all deaths in these countries every year. One in every six men aged between 40 and 44 has clinical evidence of heart disease. By the time they are 55 to 59, nearly one in three men has these symptoms.

Any part of the body can be affected by a clogged-up blood supply. If the arteries in the brain are clogged up, you get a stroke; if it's the arteries supplying the kidneys, you get high blood pressure or kidney failure. Pouring animal fat into your arteries day after day is obviously going to clog them up. It's like continually pouring lard down the plughole in the sink, then turning on the cold tap.

When autopsies were performed on American soldiers who had been killed in the Korean War, researchers were amazed by the results. Over 77 per cent of the young American soldiers had arteries which already showed evidence of atherosclerotic deposits, while Korean soldiers of the same age had clear blood vessels. At first the difference was thought to be due to race. But then they discovered that Korean soldiers who were fed a diet similar to that of the American soldiers soon developed raised blood cholesterol levels and the beginnings of atherosclerosis.

In all the worldwide studies of heart disease and strokes the results are always the same. The more animal fat a nation consumes, the more deaths it has from heart disease. The less animal fat it eats, the fewer deaths it has from heart disease.

Excess animal fat also seems to be a factor in the incidence of cancer. The number of women who get breast cancer coincides exactly with the amount of animal fat eaten in the part of the world in which they live. For example, in a Buddhist country like Thailand, where the diet is vegetarian and little animal fat is eaten, breast cancer is extremely rare. Similarly, countries with the lowest consumption of fat, such as Japan and Nigeria, have the lowest rates of uterine cancer. And countries with the highest consumption of fat, like the United Kingdom and the United States, have the highest rates of uterine cancer. Why should this be?

It seems to work like this. Animal fats in meat and dairy products raise the level of powerful, growth-promoting hormones like oestrogen and prolactin in women, and androgen in men. When the sensitive tissues which respond to these hormones – in the breast and uterus in women, in the prostate in men – are constantly bombarded by them, growth in the form of cancers can result. The more animal fat in a girl's diet, the earlier her periods will begin, and the greater will be her risk of breast cancer. The more fat that is eaten, the heavier, further apart, longer and more painful her periods become, with greater pre-menstrual difficulties, too. Diets high in meat, dairy produce and eggs also seem to delay the menopause.

As a postscript to this, women who suffer from pre-menstrual syndrome (PMS) find that the symptoms completely disappear once they stop eating animal fats and thus over-producing hormones. (This has certainly been my own experience since I have given up dairy produce in addition to not eating meat and fish.) The Women's Nutritional Advisory Service (incorporating the Pre-menstrual Tension Advisory Service; page 230) recommends a diet free from animal products.

A very similar process happens in men. Even if they do not develop cancer of the prostate, 40 per cent of men in the UK and USA have enlarged prostates by the time they are 60 years of age. In countries like Thailand, where little animal fat is eaten, it's rare to see this form of cancer.

On a lighter note, some research in Japan suggests that a pure vegetarian diet may help cure baldness in men! Baldness was unknown among Japanese men before the Second World War. After that, when they began to change to a more fatty, Western style of eating, they acquired the same rate of baldness as American and British men. This could well be related to the change in the balance of hormones caused by eating large quantities of animal fat. From what we know, it looks as if we would all be well advised to reduce our animal fat intake drastically. Ideally, we would cut it out altogether.

Too Much Protein

The human body needs protein for growth and repair of tissues – to make new hair, blood, fingernails and antibodies. Very little protein is needed for this – around 25 g (1 oz) a day. One good-sized piece of chicken can have more than 40 g (1.6 oz) of protein in it. And if you have bacon and eggs for breakfast, a cheese roll for lunch and chicken for dinner you can end up having more than 150 g (5 oz) of protein in a day.

But too much protein is bad for you. Your body can only use a little of it so your kidneys have to get rid of the rest, and this puts a great deal of extra strain on them. In order to get rid of the protein the kidneys have to draw on the body's supply of calcium: this calcium is excreted with the protein in the urine and can be measured to work out your calcium balance.

It used to be believed that our bones lost calcium only if there was not enough calcium in our diets. However it has now been shown that when protein levels are too high, the body loses more calcium than it can absorb. Even when we seem to be taking in perfectly adequate amounts of calcium our bodies can end up getting rid of too much, if our protein intake is too high.

This is particularly important in view of the widespread concern over osteoporosis, the formal name for bone mineral losses. For a person to qualify technically as having this condition they need to have lost 50 to 75 per cent of the original bone material from their skeleton. In the USA and UK one in four women in the 65-year-old age group has osteoporosis. More deaths are related to osteoporosis than are caused by breast cancer and cervical cancer combined.

Osteoporosis is caused in a number of ways, but a very important factor is excess dietary protein. The more protein a person eats, the greater the calcium that is lost. One long-term study found that with as little as 75 g (3 oz) of protein each day (less than three-quarters of what the average meat-eating Briton or American eats) more calcium is lost in the urine than is absorbed by the body from the diet – a negative calcium balance. In every study the same correspondence was found: the more protein people take in, the more calcium they lose.

The US Dairy Council sponsored a study in which one group of women drank an extra three glasses of low-fat milk every day and another group ate normally. Milk is of course rich in calcium, so they were expecting the women taking the extra milk to show increased calcium levels. At the end of a year, however, the women who drank the extra milk showed no significant increase in calcium balance. They were unable to absorb the extra calcium because of the extra protein they were getting from the milk.

Worldwide, the incidence of osteoporosis corresponds directly to the protein intake. The more protein eaten, the greater the rate of osteoporosis. World health statistics show that the condition is most common in those countries where the greatest quantities of dairy products are eaten: the United States, the United Kingdom, Sweden and Finland.

Of course there are other factors which contribute to osteoporosis as well. Women are far more prone to it than men, and small, white women who do not exercise much are the most likely to get it, as are women who have not breast-fed their babies and women who have not had children. High consumption of junk foods, excess salt, smoking and acid-forming foods also contribute. But the one predominant factor is excess protein consumption.

In a study of bone densities in the United States, researchers at Michigan State and other major universities found that, by the age of 65 in the United States, male vegetarians had an average measurable bone loss of 3 per cent; male meat-eaters 18 per cent; female vegetarians 7 per cent; and female meat-eaters 35 per cent.

Eating large amounts of protein not only greatly increases the risk of getting osteoporosis, it also seems to speed up the ageing process. It is a fact that the populations in the world who eat the most meat have the shortest life expectancy. Eskimos, Laplanders, Greenlanders and the Russian Kurgi have the highest animal flesh consumption in the world and the shortest life expectancy – often as short as 30 years.

This isn't just due to severe climatic conditions, because there are other races, living in equally severe conditions, who have life expectancies of 90 to 100 years. These are the Russian Caucasians, the Yucatan Indians, the Indian Todas and the Pakistan Hunzakuts. The cultures with the longest lifespans in the world are the Vilcambas, in the Andes of Ecuador; the Abkhasians, on the Black Sea in Russia; and the Hunzas, in the Himalayas of northern Pakistan.

What all the long-lived races have in common is that they are either totally vegetarian or very close to it. The largest group, the Hunzas, eat practically no animal products. Meat and dairy products together account for only 1.5 per cent of their total calories. And all who have seen these people remark on their energy and vigour.

All the evidence seems to show that a low-protein vegetarian diet will protect your health (particularly your bones), give you more energy, and slow down the ageing process. In other words, you will look and feel more youthful for longer, and may even increase your lifespan.

17

Too Little Fibre

It is impossible to discuss many of these diseases of too much fat and protein without mentioning another factor – too little fibre.

Fibre contains few nutrients, yet plays a vital role in our digestion. It consists of cellulose, gums and plant material such as the outer coatings of grains, the 'brown' part of brown rice and flour, the skins of potatoes, apples and other fruits.

The fibre protects the nutrients in foods, wrapping them up so that it takes time for the body to digest them. Sugars are drawn out slowly and steadily over a period of time so that the body can cope with them in an orderly way, keeping blood sugar levels even. Fibre also protects the body from fats, cholesterol and other harmful substances, by wrapping and binding them so that they are less likely to be absorbed.

As the nutrients pass along the digestive tract, the fibre holds water. This means that the contents of the gut remain smooth and soft and move easily through the bowel. As we have seen, the human gut, like the gut of any herbivore, is long and full of puckers and pouches precisely to allow for the slow extraction of nutrients from the high fibre of the typical herbivore diet.

Meat, as you will remember, contains no fibre. It also putrefies and turns carcinogenic if left to hang around in the gut for any length of time, so animals designed to eat meat regularly have a short, smooth gut. Unfortunately, it's not easy to move meat waste quickly through the human bowel because of its lack of fibre. So constipation is common. The consequent straining can cause piles and varicose veins, and, in severe cases, hiatus hernia.

Sometimes bits of dry waste matter break off during their passage through the colon. They then get stuck in little pockets in the gut which may become infected. The result is diverticular disease, which affects three out of four people in the UK and USA.

In his pioneering work on fibre, Denis Burkitt found that the incidence of constipation, haemorrhoids, hiatus hernia, diverticular diseases, spastic colons and appendicitis corresponded very closely to the amount of fibre and fat in people's diets. In fact all these diseases could be prevented (and some even cured) by a diet which is high in natural fibre and low in animal fat.

Cancer of the colon is another disease related to meat-eating. When a person eats meat year after year, the gut becomes coated with carcinogens, and cancer can eventually result. There is not a single population in the world with a high meat intake which does not have a high rate of colon cancer.

These dangers are being recognized by the American Cancer Society which is now telling people that the more meat they eat, the more likely they are to get cancer, and the more vegetables they eat, the less likely. The Bristol Centre in Britain also uses a pure vegetarian diet to help cure cancer.

Cutting out meat is a major step on the road to healthier eating. It automatically reduces your intake of animal fat and protein, while increasing your quota of fibre, thus bringing you all the benefits of health, vitality, youthfulness, and a diet that works *with* your body rather than against it.

4

What About the Nutrients?

So far we've mainly talked about foods you shouldn't eat. By now you are probably wondering what you *should* be eating. The foods on which the Green Age Diet is based can be divided into six main groups (see table opposite).

Using these ingredients, it is possible to eat varied and delicious meals including plenty of the foods which most people like best: pasta, chips, jacket potatoes, good crusty bread, rice dishes including deliciously spicy mixtures, filling vegetable and pulse soups and stews, bakes and burgers and casseroles, fresh fruit and nuts and vegetables.

But if you are not eating meat or animal products you may wonder how you will get all the essential nutrients. Most people are particularly worried about protein, iron and calcium, and whether they need to take extra vitamin supplements.

Where Will I Get Protein?

From the same place that the elephant, the horse and the cow get their protein: from grains, root vegetables, leafy green vegetables, dried beans and lentils, nuts and seeds. There is an abundance of protein in such foods.

We actually need very little protein. Experts vary on the exact amount but the range is from 2.5 to 10 per cent of our

THE SIX MAIN FOOD GROUPS

Grains and Potatoes

rice, millet, wheat, bread, bulgur wheat, oats, corn, pasta

Pulses

split red and whole green and brown lentils, chick peas, split peas, all types of beans including red kidney, cannellini beans, butterbeans, baked beans, soya beans, soya flour, soya milk, tofu

Nuts and Seeds

walnuts, hazel nuts, brazil nuts, pine nuts, almonds, pecan nuts, sunflower seeds, sesame seeds, tahini, peanuts, peanut butter

Green and Yellow Vegetables

leafy green vegetables of all types, cucumbers, green beans, salad greens, carrots, sweet potatoes, parsnips, pumpkins and squashes

Fresh Fruits

especially orange-fleshed melon and citrus fruit

Sea Vegetables and B12 Supplement

nori, dulse, kombu, hijiki, arame, wakame

daily calories. The higher figure allows for a large margin of safety for people with metabolisms that need an above-average amount. In fact the vast majority of people would easily have their needs met within that range, say at 5 per cent. It's interesting to note that human breast-milk, which nourishes babies while they are growing faster than they'll ever grow again, contains only 5 per cent protein. However, on the Green Age Diet it is very easy to get at least 10 per cent of your daily calories as protein. Look at the levels in the following table.

PERCENTAGE OF CALORIES FROM PROTEIN

Pulses	%	*Fruit*	%
mung bean sprouts	43	honeydew melon	16
tofu	43	strawberries	8
lentils	29	peach	6
kidney beans	26	banana	5
		apple	1
Vegetables			
spinach	49	*Nuts and Seeds*	
broccoli	45	pumpkin seeds	21
cauliflower	40	sunflower seeds	17
mushrooms	38	walnuts	13
cabbage	22	almonds	12
potatoes	10	cashew nuts	12
		hazel nuts	8
Grains			
wheatgerm	31		
wheat	17		
oatmeal	15		
millet	12		
barley	11		
brown rice	8		

As you can see, even if you ate only potatoes, you'd get enough protein; if you ate only cabbage, you'd get double your protein needs, and if you ate nothing but mung bean sprouts you'd get more than four times! Of course in practice you'd be getting your calories from a range of foods, but these percentages show how easy it is to get more than enough protein.

The only way an adult can possibly be deficient in protein is by eating just junk food – crisps, white bread and sweets; or by trying to live on fruit alone or on those few crops whose protein content is unusually low, such as cassava root. If a young child is fed on just grains and vegetables, it might have difficulty absorbing enough protein, due to the immaturity of its digestive system. Studies have shown that potatoes can supply 100 per cent of an infant's needs, but some grains may fall short. If a baby is breast-fed, however, there's nothing to worry about. The only other way a vegetarian can fail to meet their protein needs would be by starving.

Nevertheless you may still be wondering whether vegetable proteins contain *all* the essential nutrients. The theory of 'complete' and 'incomplete' proteins has become one of the major modern food myths. It was started by a book called *Diet for a Small Planet*, by Frances Moore Lappe. This book was published in 1971 and it showed how, by putting together two types of vegetable protein, such as grains and beans, you could end up with more protein than if you ate them separately. A case of the sum of the whole being greater than the sum of the two separate parts, or of two and two equalling five, not four! This is because the amino acid pattern in grains fits so well with that of beans that more protein can be used. But since, as we've seen, getting enough protein isn't a problem, and in fact most people have exactly the opposite problem, this balancing of proteins is irrelevant and confusing.

When Frances Moore Lappe realized the confusion she had unintentionally caused, she did her best to correct it, by including the following statement in the tenth anniversary edition of *Diet for a Small Planet*:

In 1971 I stressed protein complementarity because I assumed that the only way to get enough protein ... was to create a protein as usable by the body as animal protein. In combating the myth that meat is the only way to get high-quality protein, I reinforced another myth. I gave the impression that in order to get enough protein without meat, considerable care was needed in choosing foods. Actually, it is much easier than I thought ... [I] helped create a new myth — that to get the proteins you need without meat you have to conscientiously combine non-meat sources ... With a healthy, varied diet, concern about protein complementarity is not necessary for most of us.

In spite of all this, you may still think some meat is necessary if you are engaged in active physical work. This is another widely held belief, although in fact many athletes eat starch-based diets for energy and endurance. A number of tests have been done to compare the stamina of vegetarians and meat-eaters. In all cases the average stamina of vegetarians has been markedly greater than that of meat-eaters.

One of these tests took place at Yale University. Professor Irving Fisher compared the strength of meat-eating athletes, vegetarian athletes and ordinary sedentary vegetarians. His results, which were reported in the *Yale Medical Journal*, showed that even the sedentary vegetarians had more endurance than the meat-eaters. After analysing all the findings, Fisher concluded that the difference in endurance could only be attributed to the difference in diet.

Many top athletes have in fact been vegetarian, including Dave Scott who won the Hawaiian Ironman Triathlon four times, including three times in a row when no other athlete had won it more than once, and Olympic gold-medallists Edwin Moses and Murray Rose. One of the most dramatic successes was that of the Japanese baseball team, the Siebu Lions. This team finished last in the season, after which their new manager put them all on to a pure vegetarian diet. They then went on to win the Japanese equivalent of the World Series two years in succession!

Where Will I Get Iron and Calcium?

From the same place as the elephant, who needs plenty for its big bones and tusks. There is ample calcium in leafy green vegetables, nuts and seeds, grains and pulses. And remember, your need for calcium is not so great when you're not constantly losing it through eating too much protein (as you do when you're eating meat).

It's actually much easier to eat a balanced diet when you cut out animal products. This is because fruit, vegetables, nuts, grains and seeds all contain reasonable amounts of both iron and calcium. This is not the case with animal foods: those which are rich in iron lack calcium; while those which are rich in calcium are short of iron.

All meats (including poultry) are low in calcium because it's found in the bones, not the flesh of animals. On the other hand, they're very good sources of iron. Dairy products, which are very rich in calcium, contain little or no iron. So either you eat a lot of meat products and become calcium-deficient, or you eat a lot of dairy produce and get iron-deficient. Or you eat a lot of both and you get fat and have a heart attack!

The table overleaf shows the amount of iron and calcium in a 50-calorie serving of different foods.

The recommended daily intake of iron requires 0.43 mg of iron in every 50-calories-worth of food. So the ideal level of iron in each of these foods would be 0.43 mg. All the foods have adequate levels of iron except for milk and cheese, which are low. The non-animal foods are particularly good sources of iron.

The recommended daily intake of calcium is 800 mg. In order to reach this you need to get an average 23 mg of calcium in a 50-calorie portion of food.

IRON AND CALCIUM PER 50 CALORIE PORTION

Food	Iron mg	Calcium mg
milk	0.03	90
hard cheese	0.15	120
egg	0.68	21
chicken (and all meats)	0.5	3
broccoli	1.45	160
haricot beans	1.21	24
strawberries	1.45	31
wholewheat grains	0.95	11

The milk and cheese are excellent sources of calcium, the egg is a little low and meat is very lacking. In order to get your daily quota of calcium from just chicken, you'd have to have 300 servings, or 15,000 calories! The only non-animal food which is low in calcium is wholewheat grains. Actually wheat is an adequate source of calcium if you are eating a diet which is modest in protein, like the Green Age Diet. The recommended calcium level is based on a high-protein diet; on a healthier, low-protein diet the amount of calcium needed each day is only 250–400 mg (less than recommended level) which would make wheat adequate.

Do I Need to Take Vitamin Supplements?

The only vitamin which is problematical when you're eating little or no animal produce is B12. The body stores B12 in the liver, and has enough reserves to last for ten to twenty years. Also, there are bacteria within the human body which make vitamin B12, in the saliva, the bile and within the intestines. Some people can absorb this B12 and live off it.

This vitamin is also found in some sea vegetables and fermented soya products (such as miso) and some products are fortified with it. However, to be on the safe side, if you're on a low-animal-product diet for more than two to three years, or if you're pregnant or nursing, then a B12 tablet three times a week is a good idea. (See below for more on pregnant and nursing mothers.)

Apart from B12, vitamin supplements aren't necessary if you're eating properly. The diseases we have in developed countries are diseases of *excess*, not deficiency. Do you know anyone who has scurvy? Pellagra? Beri-beri? But how many people do you know who are overweight or have heart problems? These are caused by eating too much of the wrong foods. Eat a good healthy diet and trust your body to use the nutrients.

An added bonus of the Green Age Diet is that it is naturally high in vitamin C which helps to prevent some forms of cancer. It's difficult to get a high enough level of this vitamin on a meat diet and there is no evidence that taking supplements has the same effect. It's the way the vitamin is contained in the foods which seems to do the good.

Pregnant and Nursing Mothers, Babies and Children

People sometimes wonder, naturally enough, whether a diet containing no meat or fish, and little or no dairy produce, is suitable for a pregnant or nursing mother, and for children. With our very meat-orientated Western culture, it's easy to forget that people all over the world have also produced healthy babies, on a vegan diet, throughout history.

A properly balanced vegan diet consists of three meals a day, based on two to four 100 g (4 oz) servings of grains or potatoes, one to two 100 g (4 oz) servings of cooked pulses, three to six pieces of fruit, especially citrus fruit and orange-fleshed melons, one to three 100 g (4 oz) servings of green and yellow vegetables and 25–75 g (1–3 oz) nuts each day, plus sea vegetables and yeast or yeast extract three or four times a week. Such a diet will provide all the main nutrients needed by a pregnant or nursing mother, with the possible exception of vitamin B12. A B12 supplement should be taken three times a week, and, to be on the safe side, a good well-balanced multivitamin tablet two to three times a week. (When choosing a vitamin tablet, make sure that all the ingredients are made from plant, not animal, sources.)

Breast-milk is the perfect food for a baby, and, again, the vegan or vegetarian diet can supply all the nutrients needed by a nursing mother. In fact, nutritional requirements during nursing are almost the same as during pregnancy except that a little less protein is needed. Trust your own body and your own instincts to guide you; it will do so more and more as it becomes strong, clean and healthy on a pure vegan or vegetarian diet. If you cannot breast-feed, choose a vitamin-fortified soya milk such as Plamil or the special vegan baby milk which Granose make.

It's very important not to hurry the introduction of solid foods. Breast-milk contains all that a baby needs until it is six months old. After that, little tastes of different foods can be given before a breast-feed. Mashed or puréed ripe fruits such as banana, peach, pear, apricot and avocado make excellent first foods; also cooked and sieved vegetables, particularly mashed potato and carrot. A little freshly squeezed orange juice, diluted with filtered or spring water, can also be given. When I weaned my youngest daughter, Claire, at 6½ months, the first food I gave her was a taste of lentil soup, like the one on page 139, and she also had a lot of mashed baked beans, both of which she loved.

From these beginnings, a baby gradually has more and more solid food and less breast-milk, although feeding continues to be important for emotional satisfaction even when the baby is getting most of its nutrients from solid food. (Claire had her last feed from me when she was just two!)

Because vegetarian and vegan foods are high in fibre, it's important to make sure that a young child does not have such a bulky diet that he or she cannot manage to eat enough to get sufficient nutrients. Some experts, for instance, suggest using a 'brown' rather than a 100 per cent wholewheat bread for children under two. Include some concentrated sources of protein such as wheatgerm, tofu, powdered nuts or nut butters (such as peanut butter), tahini or puréed or mashed lentil and bean dishes rather than very chewy ones. Potatoes, baked in their jackets, then mashed, are an almost perfect food for children of all ages, and full-fat soya milk to drink until the baby is three years old. Yeast extract is another popular and nutritious food, and carrot sticks and fresh and dried fruits for snacks.

For more details on this subject, see my book *Rose Elliot's Mother and Baby Book*, and Dr Michael Klaper's *Pregnancy, Children and the Vegan Diet* (page 231).

5

The Storecupboard

The Green Age storecupboard consists of grains and pulses, nuts and seeds, fresh fruits and vegetables and sea vegetables, herbs and flavourings, all in as natural a state as possible. Here are some notes on the various products, what to look out for and how to use them.

Grains

It's worth getting to know all kinds of grains and the products made from them: oats and oatcakes, barley, millet, rice, wheat, wholewheat flour and breads (including pitta bread, rolls and chapattis), pasta, cracked wheat (burghul or bulgur wheat), buckwheat (which is strictly speaking a seed but classified under grains), rye grains, rye bread and crispbreads, cornmeal, tortillas, tortilla chips and couscous.

Grains are easy to cook (pages 178–9), filling and nourishing to eat, and can form the basis of many excellent meals. Add vegetables to them to make a main course, or serve them alongside a vegetable dish such as a stir-fry, succulent ratatouille or chilli to make a more substantial meal.

Grains are best in their brownest, least refined form because they retain the most goodness and take less energy to produce. In this form, incidentally, many of them can be sprouted in the same way as pulses (see page 165), with the same health benefits.

Whenever possible, choose organically grown grains and flours, and buy in as large a quantity as is practical for you, to save on packaging. If they are kept in a dry place, whole grains will keep for a year, flours for three to four months.

The basic grain to start with is brown rice. Cook it simply, without any salt, and eat it with a few steamed or stir-fried vegetables or some raisins scattered into it and you really begin to appreciate how delicious and wholesome this grain is. Brown basmati rice, if you can get it, is more expensive, but even nicer than ordinary brown rice.

Once you're really familiar with brown rice, try some of the other grains. Millet, for instance, cooks in 20–25 minutes and makes good pilafs, salads and burgers. Bulgur wheat is another useful one, and this doesn't need cooking at all if you're eating it cold with salads; if you want it hot, it only takes 10 to 15 minutes.

Dried Beans and Lentils

There are many varieties, some of the best being whole green lentils, brown lentils, split red lentils, split peas, chick peas, soya beans, mung beans, butterbeans and red kidney beans. These dried seeds of leguminous plants are an ancient and almost perfect food. One 450 g (1 lb) bag of dried beans or lentils, when soaked and cooked (pages 166–7), produces over three times its weight in ready-to-eat, high-fibre, low-fat food, which can be made into delicious soups, stews and savoury dishes. Useful pulses to start with are split orange lentils, green lentils, red kidney beans and chick peas.

From an ecological point of view, it is better to buy minimally packaged pulses in their dried form and soak and cook them yourself rather than using canned ones. However, canned red kidney beans and chick peas are a useful standby in the storecupboard. Try to choose varieties with the fewest additives in the form of sugar, salt and so on.

Most pulses can also be sprouted (page 165) and this increases their volume and vitamin content enormously. The vitamin C in soya beans, for instance, increases by over 500 per cent when they are sprouted. Because of their cheapness, the way they increase in volume, and their high nutritional content, sprouts are the most economical food known.

Some people find cooked pulses indigestible. If you have found this in the past, you will probably discover that you can eat them when they're sprouted. This is because the sprouting process begins to break down the starches into simple sugars which are much easier to digest.

Sprouted pulses, grains and seeds are known as 'biogenic' foods because they are germinating and full of life-force. For this reason, alone, apart from the other advantages I've mentioned, they're worth getting to know. And, as Leslie Kenton points out in *The Biogenic Diet*, if you've grown them yourself in pure spring water, you know they're one food in your diet that's organic and additive-free.

Another pulse product is tofu, or bean curd, made from soya beans. This is a high-protein food which has been eaten in China for thousands of years. The firm variety of tofu can be sliced and soaked in a marinade, or sprinkled with tamari, added to casseroles, burgers and bakes, or fried; the smooth or 'silken' type can be whizzed into dressings, dips, toppings and creamy fools. Although it tastes quite bland, tofu absorbs other flavours well. You can buy it from healthfood shops, oriental food stores, and an increasing number of ordinary supermarkets and food shops. Once the packet has been opened, store the tofu in water in the fridge, changing the water daily.

Nuts and Seeds

These, too, are little powerhouses of vitality, and like pulses and grains, some of them can be sprouted. They include almonds, brazil nuts, hazel nuts, walnuts, pecan nuts, cashew nuts, pine nuts, coconuts and pistachios; sunflower, pumpkin and sesame seeds; also, for sprouting, alfalfa seeds, fenugreek and mustard seeds.

All the nuts, together with sunflower, pumpkin and sesame seeds, can be chopped and sprinkled over salads, mueslis and cooked vegetable dishes; or they can be made into savoury loaves and burgers (pages 191–3). They can also be whizzed up with filtered or spring water to make delicious frothy white milks (pages 108–9, 112) which make an excellent replacement for dairy milk, especially for pouring over breakfast cereal. They are very concentrated foods and a little goes a long way. Make sure you buy them really fresh, as rancid nuts aren't good for you. The best place to store nuts is in the fridge or freezer, if you've got room.

Of course there are many different types of nuts to choose from. But in *The Green Consumer Guide* the authors put in a special plea for us to use brazil nuts, because a greater demand might save some of the brazil-nut trees in the rainforests which are at present being destroyed. Peanuts are perhaps the most common, though they are not true nuts. They're actually classed as pulses even though they're cooked and eaten more like nuts. Chestnuts, too, are different, being much starchier and less fatty than true nuts.

Cashew nuts and almonds make delicious creams (page 108), and of course there are nut butters too. If you like peanut butter, choose one without emulsifiers. When the oil gathers on top, you can pour it off and use it for cooking (thus reducing the calories in the peanut butter – soften it with a little water if necessary). Alternatively, if you're not concerned about the extra calories, you can simply stir it in. Sesame cream, called tahini, is a creamy purée which you can buy from healthfood shops or shops which sell Middle Eastern foods. Actually I prefer the Middle Eastern variety which is paler and thinner than other types. Cypressa make a good one. Tahini is rich, with a slightly bitter taste, and a little goes a long way. It's used in hummus (page 118) and other dips and dressings and can be spread on bread. It keeps well in the fridge.

Vegetables

Along with grains and fruits, fresh vegetables are a vital part of the Green Age Diet. They can, and should, be eaten in plentiful quantities.

Scientists are finding increasing evidence of the protective qualities of enzymes and vitamins in both fruit and vegetables. For instance, beta-carotene – the colouring which is found in dark green, orange and yellow fruits and vegetables, and which our body converts into vitamin A – has powerful antioxidant qualities, combating carcinogens in our gut, lungs and reproductive organs. Green and yellow, or yellow-orange vegetables, are especially rich in beta-carotene.

There is also evidence that vitamin C in peppers, tomatoes and many vegetables (as well as in citrus fruits, peaches and apricots) offers protection from cancer. Just taking supplements of vitamin A or C does not have the same effect.

Most people are aware of the importance of vitamins but not so many are familiar with substances known as indoles, found in members of the cabbage family. In extensive research and experiments these have been shown to inhibit the formation of tumours. In addition, researchers have shown that seeds, such as dried beans and lentils, and grains, also contain various substances which inhibit the formation of tumours.

34

Garlic has been used in healing for thousands of years and is a potent antibiotic. In laboratory experiments, it was found that one active substance in garlic, diallyl sulphide, offered significant protection against cancer. Furthermore, a number of experiments over the last ten years in India, Pakistan and the US have found that garlic has beneficial effects on blood cholesterol. A daily dose of garlic reduced total blood cholesterol, while decreasing the 'bad' or LDL cholesterol (low-density lipoproteins), and increasing the 'good' or HDL cholesterol (high-density lipoproteins).

Onions, too, have been found to raise the HDL cholesterol and lower the LDL cholesterol, although the total cholesterol in the blood has stayed about the same. They are also a rich natural source of prostaglandin A-1, a hormone known to lower blood pressure.

So onions and garlic are clearly worth eating on a daily basis – perhaps an onion and one to two garlic cloves. This daily consumption of onion and garlic would be considered normal in countries such as Italy, Greece and the South of France, where most dishes begin with the gentle sautéeing of onions and garlic in olive oil – as indeed does vegetarian cookery.

This may be one reason for the low level of heart disease in these countries. So be liberal in your use of onions and garlic, in both cooked and raw dishes. If you're worried about the effect on your breath, chew some parsley or drink some water with a squeeze of lemon juice in it.

Choose organic vegetables whenever possible. All vegetables need careful washing, particularly if they're not organic and may have residues of pesticides and fungicides. Lettuces can have particularly high residues of fungicide. Wash leafy vegetables thoroughly in several changes of cold water. Some vegetables, including peppers, cucumbers and aubergines, may be coated with a wax to make them shiny. Scrub them thoroughly, in hot water with a dash of biodegradable washing-up liquid, or, if in doubt, remove the skins.

Fresh Fruit

Fruit is cleansing and light to digest. Although it seems acid, it actually has the effect of making the digestive system more alkaline. Citrus fruits are particularly valuable because of their vitamin C content, and orange melons for their high levels of vitamin A.

Apart from their nutritional importance, some types of fruit are extremely versatile. For example, avocado adds richness and smoothness to meals and is a kind of cheese/butter/mayonnaise replacement, I find, particularly in salad meals. It's also an excellent source of nourishment, and can be used freely as long as you're not trying to lose weight. Add a slice or two to a salad sandwich or pitta pocket; slice it into hot pasta or rice dishes just before serving; or blend it into creamy dips and dressings which can replace mayonnaise.

Exotic fruits and vegetables like, in Britain, avocado make a pleasant change and a treat, although in its strictest interpretation Green Age cooking is based on local, seasonal, organic produce. This means the produce is cheaper and resources are not used transporting or processing it.

As with vegetables, choose organically grown fruit whenever you can, and wash it carefully if you are going to eat the skin. Wash it in plain water, or water with a dash of biodegradable washing-up liquid, and scrub citrus fruits and apples which look as if they have been coated with wax in hot water and biodegradable washing-up liquid. Sorry as I am to say this, you are probably better advised not to use the skins of fruits if you're in doubt.

Dried Fruits

Dried fruits are an excellent source of concentrated nourishment and make a wonderful snack when your energy level is low and you're feeling in need of a boost. However, you need to take some care when buying them.

Dried fruits are often treated with sulphur dioxide to preserve their colour and then coated with mineral oil to keep them shiny and free-moving in the packet. Look for sun-dried fruits packed without preservatives and oils, and wash them carefully before using. They often appear less appetizing than the preserved and coated variety (for instance the little wizened Hunza or Afghan apricots as compared to the plump orange type), but as soon as you taste them, you'll realize how much better the brown ones taste.

According to Jane Grigson, in her *Book of Fruit*, dried dates can be treated with a number of chemicals before they are sold. First they may be dusted with an insecticide called Malathion, washed with detergent and then coated with glycerine or some similar substance to make them look shiny. In their book, *C for Chemicals*, Michael Birkin and Brian Price mention that the World Health Organization lists this chemical as 'slightly hazardous' and say that 'there is some evidence of mutagenicity [tendency to produce genetic changes] and possible carcinogenicity in animal tests'.

Sea Vegetables

The idea of using sea vegetables, or seaweed, may not sound very appealing but they have been used for thousands of years in Chinese and Japanese cookery, and by island-dwellers in many parts of the world.

Seaweed is a particularly good food because it is the richest vegetable source of iodine which is needed for the efficient working of the thyroid gland. In addition, iodine gives some protection against the effects of radiation. Sea vegetables are also rich in other minerals, including iron, calcium, magnesium, selenium and potassium.

Various types of dried seaweed are available at healthfood and oriental shops, or by post from Clearspring (page 229). I think the best one to start with is nori because it is very flavoursome and easy to prepare. It looks like sheets of black paper, and can be eaten as it is, or used as a wrapping for any tasty morsel, particularly sweet vinegared rice to make vegetarian sushi. But I think it's nicest toasted. Just hold a sheet of nori over a gas flame or electric burner for a few seconds until it crackles and crispens. Then eat it as it is, or crumble it over a salad, vegetable dish or soup. Delicious!

Other sea vegetables to try are arame, dulse, hiziki, kombu and wakame. These need soaking in water for 5–10 minutes to soften them before chopping them up and adding them to salad or stir-fry. They can also be added to soups to give a pleasantly salty taste of the sea.

Herbs, Spices and Flavourings

These add interest and variety to grain, cereal and pulse dishes; to soups, salads, savouries and side dishes. They make cooking a creative pleasure and eating a joy. Build up a collection of flavourings gradually, as you try new recipes, and don't be afraid to experiment! Here's a list of some of the basics.

SEA SALT

Use this sparingly, in place of ordinary table or cooking salt. I like Tidman's, the flaky kind that you can crush up in your fingers.

TAMARI

A naturally fermented soy sauce available from healthfood shops. It has a deliciously rich, savoury taste, and adds colour as well as flavour.

MISO

Another fermented soya bean product, this is a brown or reddish savoury paste which is particularly rich in nutrients. It is added to soups, sauces and savoury dishes at the end of the cooking time (to preserve the enzymes) or used to make a clear, Oriental-style soup. It can also be spread on bread (like yeast extract) and used raw in dips.

YEAST EXTRACT

Like miso, a useful flavouring for savouries, soups, sauces, stews and so on. Choose the brand with the flavour you like best but read the label to check on additives. Some yeast extracts are fortified with B12.

VEGETABLE BOUILLON

Useful for flavouring soups and casseroles. My favourites are Marigold Vegetable Bouillon, in a tub in the form of granules, and Hügli Bouillon Concentrate which is a paste. Buy them from healthfood shops, or the Marigold one can be ordered direct (page 229).

HERBS AND SPICES

Fresh herbs are delicious, particularly in salads. The ones I find most useful are parsley, chives, mint, tarragon and fresh basil. Others which I often use when available are fresh coriander, rosemary, flat-leaf parsley, curry plant, thyme, dill, lovage, sage, marjoram, salad burnet, bay and fennel. Herbs are rewarding, attractive plants to grow, and many of them are very easy to cultivate.

But never let lack of fresh herbs put you off making a dish. Dried ones are handy, too, particularly mixed herbs, rosemary, thyme, bay, oregano and basil. Useful spices include whole nutmegs to grate when needed; coriander, ground and whole; cumin, ground and whole; paprika, cinnamon sticks, turmeric and medium curry powder; and of course black peppercorns, to use in a peppermill.

Buy herbs and spices loose in small quantities, or at least without elaborate packaging, from a shop with a quick turnover, and store them in reusable glass jars.

MUSTARD

Mustard is good in salad dressings and marinades. Grey Poupon Dijon mustard is my favourite; Meaux mustard, with its grainy texture, is also mild and delicious.

OLIVES AND BLACK OLIVE PÂTÉ

A lovely piquant addition to many dishes. Buy the olives loose from the delicatessen – take your own jar to put them in if possible to cut down on packaging. A jar of black olive pâté is a delicious treat to keep in the fridge – I think it's the Green Age answer to caviar! Try it spread on small savoury crackers or Oatcakes (page 213), or as a piquant garnish on anything from avocado salad to pizza.

SWEETENERS

It's best from the health point of view to eat less sugar and I find that simply not having much in the house is a very good way of doing this! On the other hand, I'm not one for too much martyrdom or faddishness and I don't mind the occasional indulgence. In fact I think sugar does you far less harm than animal fat. A good wholesome fruit cake made with a little dark brown sugar and sun-dried fruits, or a piece of parkin made with wholewheat flour, oatmeal, honey and molasses sugar, are not going to do you much harm at all. Yeast-based cakes are particularly good because they have less fat and sugar in them. If you feel like eating something sweet, think in terms of a wholewheat currant bun, a thick slice of good wholewheat bread spread with honey or (preferably low-sugar) jam, a few raisins or sun-dried apricots, or some fresh fruit. You could even have some sticks of raw carrot – especially if you want to lose weight. It's surprising how sweet these taste when you've stopped eating sugar for a while (see page 70 for more ideas along these lines).

When you're buying honey, choose 'raw' organic honey that has not been heat-treated. You will probably need to go to a healthfood shop for this. (Some vegans do not eat honey.) Buy the darkest, stickiest brown sugar that you can find – Barbados muscovado. This contains traces of minerals, including iron, and some B vitamins.

Other useful sweeteners to try are maple syrup (read the label because 'maple-flavoured syrup' is not the same thing), date syrup and rice syrup.

Drinks

WATER

Pure, fresh water is the healthiest drink, though sadly this simple necessity of life is getting harder and harder to come by. One possibility is filtering your water at home (see page 53 for more about this). Another is to buy bottled spring water, although bottling water and then using valuable energy to transport it across the globe is not a very ecologically sound process!

If you are buying bottled water, glass bottles are better than plastic, particularly if the bottles are returnable or you can take them to a bottle bank for recycling. Plastic bottles contribute to pollution problems because they are so difficult to dispose of. In addition, it has been found that substances from the plastic can leach into the water.

I have suggested the use of spring water in the recipes, but of course you can use ordinary tap water if you are in an area where this is clean and pure.

FRUIT AND VEGETABLE JUICES

Freshly squeezed or pressed juices are cleansing and good for you, when taken in moderation. A glass of freshly made fruit juice is an excellent way to start the day and fresh fruit or vegetable juices are good before a meal. The next best thing to home-made juices are ones made from organic fruit and vegetables and processed by low-heat methods. These are available in bottles from healthfood shops. Be wary of juices (and milk or soya milk) packaged in cartons, as dioxins have been found in them. And if the cartons are lined with aluminium, this may get into the liquid. So bottles are best.

TEA AND COFFEE

Standard advice from health experts is that you should cut down on tea and coffee – something which I've never found easy to do. Buy tea loose instead of in teabags to avoid the dioxins in the paper from which the bags are made. Similarly, make coffee in a cafetière, jug or permanent filter, to avoid the dioxins in paper filters.

Ground coffee is better than instant coffee from the green as well as the flavour point of view because instant coffee takes so much energy to produce. Many experts consider that real coffee is also a healthier option than highly processed, additive-laden instant coffee. Oxfam shops and Traidcraft (page 229, 230) sell coffee for which the producers in the Third World have received a fair price.

It's worth experimenting with other caffeine-free beverages. You could try dandelion coffee or other drinks made from roasted grains, and there are some delicious herb teas made by Celestial Seasonings (my favourite), and others. One of the nicest ways of making herb tea is to chop up some fresh herbs (such as mint, sage or lemon balm), put them in a teapot and cover with boiling water. Strain into cups and drink with a dash of honey or a thin slice of lemon.

WINE

If you fancy it, a little wine is in keeping with the Green Age Diet. In fact there is evidence to suggest that drinking wine with meals is not harmful and may even be beneficial to your health. Studies in both Britain and America have shown that people who drink up to two glasses of wine a day are less likely to suffer from heart disease than non-drinkers and heavy drinkers. And a report from the British Medical Research

Council published in 1979 in *The Lancet* states that there is a 'very strong relationship between wine consumption and low rate of death from heart disease'.

Organic wines, produced from unsprayed grapes and without additional chemicals, are becoming more widely available, and you can find out further details from Henry Doubleday Research Association, or from Vintage Roots (page 229, 230).

Fats and Oils

Fats are classed according to how saturated they are. Saturated fats are found mainly in animal products such as butter and cheese, whereas polyunsaturated fats mainly occur in vegetable oils, margarine, nuts, seeds and some pulses and grains. Monosaturated fat is found particularly in olive oil. All fats are mixtures of saturated, polyunsaturated and monosaturated fatty acids. In addition, saturated animal fats contain large amounts of cholesterol.

Cholesterol is a fat which is in every animal's cells, including those of our own body. There is no cholesterol in any vegetable product, including nuts, cereals and grains. Although there are some saturated vegetable fats – coconut oil, palm oil and cocoa butter – none of them contains any cholesterol.

We need cholesterol for important body processes, but our body produces all the cholesterol it needs. This is carried round our bloodstream in substances called lipoproteins. These lipoproteins are made up of a mixture of protein and fatty acids. There are two main kinds: low-density lipoproteins (LDLs) and high-density lipoproteins (HDLs). The LDLs carry the cholesterol around the body, and, if the levels are too high, deposit it on the artery walls. The HDLs take the cholesterol from the arteries to the liver to be excreted in the bile.

Swapping saturated fats for polyunsaturated oils such as corn oil and sunflower oil is not a good idea because polyunsaturates remove the 'good' cholesterol, the HDLs, as well as the 'bad' LDLs. Also, as polyunsaturates are broken down in the body there are fears that they may produce compounds known as 'free radicals'. Free radicals are thought to cause premature ageing and some cancers. So eating a lot of polyunsaturated oils may increase the risk of cancer.

However, olive oil, which is monosaturated, seems to be beneficial. The Greeks and Italians eat large quantities of olive oil but have low levels of blood cholesterol and a low rate of heart attacks. Olive oil appears to take out the 'bad' cholesterol, the LDLs, but leave the 'good' cholesterol, the HDLs.

The quality of olive oil is judged by the oleic acid content and by the colour, flavour and aroma. Extra virgin olive oil must not have more than 1 per cent acidity; and virgin olive oil not more than 4 per cent. 'Pure' olive oil has higher acidity than this so it has been refined to remove natural impurities, then blended with a little virgin oil to improve the flavour. Like wine, olive oils from different countries have different flavours. Many experts consider Italian oils, generally from Tuscany, to be the best, but the quality varies from year to year depending on the olive harvest.

In general, and for dishes where you don't want a strong flavour, a pure olive oil is best. Plagniol is a good reliable one, or Menucci. For other purposes use a good commercial virgin oil like L'Olivier. When you're feeling very rich you might like to splurge out on an estate-bottled extra virgin oil such as Piero de Monzi or Colonna from Italy or Le Vieux Moulin from France and keep it for extra-special uncooked dishes where the flavour will really shine through.

Olive oil can be used for deep-frying, although it's not good for your health to have deep-fried food, or indeed any fried food, too often. Burgers can be baked on a lightly oiled baking sheet (pages 170–71), then blotted dry on paper, and you can make excellent low-fat chips in the oven (page 164). Even samosas and spring rolls can be brushed with oil and baked. But if you do want to deep-fry for the occasional treat, the healthiest way is to buy a cheap olive oil, deep-fry in several batches in a medium-sized saucepan (so that you don't have to use too much oil) and then throw the oil away afterwards.

Many natural health experts consider that butter is preferable to margarine. However if you use olive oil as your basic fat, as I have suggested, and get used to the taste of good bread without fat on it, you will be using butter or margarine in such small quantities that I doubt whether it really matters which you choose.

If you are choosing a margarine as a butter replacement, choose a really good-quality pure polyunsaturated vegetable margarine such as Vitaquell.

No-added-sugar jam, marmalade, low-sugar spreads, yeast extract, miso, peanut butter or tahini can all be put straight on to bread without a layer of butter. Sandwiches are fine made with unbuttered bread, or with a little yeast extract or mustard. Garlic bread (page 137) is excellent made with olive oil. And really good fresh bread, especially home-made bread, is delicious without any fat.

Creamed coconut is a hard, white fat which, although saturated, is occasionally useful in spiced savoury dishes and can be made into a delicious cream (page 109).

Dairy Produce

Eating meat and fish on any regular basis is alien to the Green Age Diet. The same applies to eating large quantities of dairy produce, although small amounts of butter (preferably unsalted), natural goat's milk yogurt, free-range eggs, cream and light cheeses, can be included if you feel the need for them.

Cow's milk is not good for anyone, as I have already explained, and the more you can cut down on it, the better. Use soya milk for recipes where necessary and replace milk shakes with chilled fruit juice, nut milks, sparkling spring water, or fruit shakes (pages 110–12). Discover the pleasure of taking hot drinks without milk: black coffee, weak tea without milk, or herb teas are far more refreshing than milky ones.

A Note on Packaging

You should always try to buy locally grown produce, in season. Most goods are over-packaged and every polythene bag, wrapper or expanded polystyrene container has to be disposed of and is adding to the earth's pollution.

Choose products which are unwrapped, simply packed, or wrapped in biodegradable cellophane (mainly from healthfood shops) where possible. Products packaged in returnable or recyclable glass bottles and jars are better than plastic ones. Some string bags or a canvas shopping bag avoid the need for plastic supermarket carrier bags.

One way of cutting down on packaging is by buying in bulk, but this is only feasible if you know that you will have a steady demand for a product and you have somewhere convenient to store it! Or you might like to consider joining – or forming – a local wholefoods cooperative. If you order in bulk and then split the order up between several people, you get the price advantages of bulk buying without the storage problems, and, if you collect your goods in reusable containers, you save on packaging. Contact your local Friends of the Earth group to find out whether there are any wholefood cooperatives in your area.

Empty bottles, tins and newspapers can be recycled. Again, you can find out more about this from your local Friends of the Earth group, or by writing to the address on page 229.

A Note on Irradiation

Food irradiation is a method of preserving food by exposing it to large doses of ionizing radiation. These delay the natural ripening process and kill pests and micro-organisms. There is also some evidence that the process may produce 'free radicals', which have been shown to speed up the ageing process and cause genetic damage and cancer. Whether or not this is the case, irradiation destroys enzymes in foods and may remove other subtle properties about which we know little as yet.

As Dr Malcolm Carruthers, Director of Clinical Laboratory Services and Consultant Chemical Pathologist at the Maudsley and Royal Bethlem Hospitals, says in his Foreword to Leslie and Susannah Kenton's book, *Raw Energy*: 'Nutritionally aware physicians are few and far between, especially when it comes to factors such as the subtle energies of living plants and plant enzymes ...' And many natural therapists, including Dr Bircher Benner, have maintained that plants have a special healing and revitalizing quality derived from the effect of the sunlight on their leaves. What would irradiation do to this?

In my view, irradiation is totally out of line with a natural healthy approach to food. I hope that a test will be developed for checking whether foods have been irradiated and that irradiated food will be clearly labelled so that we can avoid buying it.

6

Equipment

Small Items

The equipment needed for Green Age cooking is simple, but getting it right can save time in the long run. A good sharp knife – a genuine Sabatier one with the blade continuing up inside the handle, and a steel for keeping it sharp – is top of the list and definitely worth the extra money. The best all-purpose length of blade is about 13 cm/5 inches. Always wash and dry it immediately after use, to avoid rusting.

A lighter, stainless-steel knife with a serrated blade, the same length, is also useful for cutting delicate fruits such as peaches and avocados, which may get a metallic flavour from the steel knife.

The other essentials are a sharp, swivel-blade potato peeler, a box grater, a lemon squeezer, a measuring jug, one or two wooden spoons, a good solid wooden chopping board (at least 38 × 30 cm/15 × 12 inches), but see the note on page 56, and a selection of mixing bowls, preferably glass or the traditional ceramic type.

Pots and Pans

The material which your pots and pans are made from is important because tiny particles can get into the food, especially acidic foods such as rhubarb or home-made jams and chutneys which require slow cooking over a long period. Aluminium pans and teapots, for instance, are considered by many to be a health hazard because the aluminium can leach out and cause brain disorders such as Alzheimer's disease. I think it is worth replacing aluminium pans as soon as funds allow.

Teflon and non-stick coverings are also dubious because of the toxic fumes which they can release at high temperatures and the particles which may break off as the coating becomes worn.

Heavy, good-quality, stainless-steel saucepans are better, but need careful cleaning. Enamel-coated iron pans such as the Le Creuset range are probably the best of all, although they are very expensive (and heavy to use). If you have any of the older Le Creuset pans the underside of the lids may be coloured and it's important that these shouldn't come into contact with food as they may leach out cadmium.

Toughened glass saucepans are safe, although I have not found these very convenient to use, as food burns so easily. Terracotta is also safe as long as it is not finished with a glaze containing lead.

A stainless-steel pressure-cooker is a very useful piece of equipment, reducing the cooking time of pulses and grains enormously. It is also wonderful for making warming, filling vegetable or lentil soups in, literally, a few minutes.

At the other extreme, one of those slow-cookers which used to be so popular a few years ago is good for saving on heat if you want to cook pulses and grains over several hours. A wide-neck vacuum flask, or a haybox, which a friend of mine uses constantly to produce a wide range of delicious meals, also provides excellent ways of cooking with the minimum of power. But if you're cooking red kidney beans by any of these slow methods, do remember to boil them hard in a saucepan for 10 minutes first to destroy any potentially harmful enzymes.

In addition to these pots and pans, it's useful to build up a collection of ovenproof casseroles in different shapes and sizes. Seek out interesting and unusual ones made by individual craftsmen, but make sure that the glazes used are safe and leadfree.

Food Processors

It's the chopping, grating and sieving which takes the time when you're cooking with natural foods. So a good, robust food processor is a great boon. Be sure to choose one that is large enough for your family, particularly if you want to liquidize soups or knead bread (which a food processor does very well).

Freezers and Refrigerators

A large refrigerator is useful for storing fresh vegetables so that you don't have to shop so often. I keep all perishable fruits and vegetables (except potatoes, onions and hard-skinned squashes) in mine. If you have a freezer, of course, you can save a great deal of time by making double quantities of favourite dishes and cooking large batches of pulses, so that you always have them to hand and do not need to resort to the more environmentally costly canned ones.

At the time of writing, all refrigerators made in the UK contain chlorofluorocarbons (CFCs) and will continue to do so until 1991, although most manufacturers have now reduced the CFCs contained in them by 50 per cent. These CFCs do no harm while the refrigerator is in use because they are contained in a sealed unit. However, when refrigerators are thrown away, the CFCs escape into the atmosphere, damaging the ozone layer and adding to the greenhouse effect.

At present, there are no plans for the safe disposal of refrigerators. But if you have to replace an old refrigerator, it is worth asking the manufacturer for their advice on safe disposal, and whether they have a policy for collecting and recycling the CFCs. Public pressure is an important factor in getting them to implement such policies. Safer refrigerators are also being developed, which should be less threatening to the atmosphere. In the meantime it seems best to hold on to your old refrigerator for as long as possible, until the CFCs can be safely recycled and the new, ozone-friendly refrigerators are available.

Dishwashers

If you are buying a dishwasher, look for one like those made by AEG which have a spray system to keep the consumption of water and power to the minimum. (The same applies to washing machines.) And whether you are washing dishes by machine or by hand, more and more biodegradable, phosphate-free dishwasher powders and washing-up liquids are coming on to the market. However some manufacturers simply want to cash in on our concern over the environment, so don't be misled by spurious or irrelevant claims.

Ovens

Look for a really well-insulated oven, to conserve heat and use less energy.

Many natural health experts have serious reservations about microwave cooking. As with irradiated food, no one knows quite what effect the microwaves have on the food. Microwaving may interfere with the vital and intangible 'life-force' of fresh foods – but on the other hand it may not. No one really knows. Although I recognize the usefulness of a microwave oven (and I do indeed possess one myself) I have an uneasy feeling about it and am really happier sticking to the traditional methods of cooking, and eating a good proportion of food raw.

Water Purifiers

Many people are concerned about the increasing evidence of chemical residues in our water. It may be polluted with nitrates and pesticides used on the land, solvents from industry, antibiotics from the slurry of intensively reared animals, phosphates from detergents, and drugs and hormones excreted by humans, particularly oestrogen from birth-control pills.

On top of all this, aluminium is added at treatment plants to make the water clearer, and some water authorities add chlorine and fluoride, both of which have been linked to cancer and genetic defects. In older houses with lead pipes, lead also gets into the water. It's worth finding out the facts from your environmental health department if you think your system may have lead pipes. If so, always let the water run for several minutes in the morning so that you are not drinking water which has been in the pipes overnight.

Various types of water filter are available but at the time of writing none is wholly satisfactory. Plumbed-in water purifiers which use activated carbon filters can become breeding grounds for bacteria, making the water worse than it was before. Another type which works by reverse osmosis is effective at removing chemicals, but takes out the good ones, such as calcium and magnesium, along with the bad. Water purified by distillation is clean but expensive to produce and insipid to drink.

I hope that a really effective system, for plumbing in under the sink, will soon become available. If you're thinking of buying one, do look at the details carefully and get advice from an organization like the Green Farm Nutrition Centre (page 229). There are at present no official standards for water filters and with increased public concern over water there are likely to be some dubious or even potentially dangerous filtration systems reaching the market.

In the meantime, I personally use one of the jug water filters, which are said to be moderately effective. With these, it is important to renew the filters very frequently. If you tot up roughly how many times you use the filter each day, you may be surprised at just how frequently! If you don't change the filter often enough, it begins to put the heavy metals back into the water and could be dangerous.

Paper Goods

Paper kitchen towels, aluminium foil, clingfilm and polythene bags are useful items which most of us take for granted. Yet they are costly in terms of the environment and also contain health hazards. Paper towels (and many white paper goods ranging from teabags and coffee filters to lavatory rolls, tampons and disposable nappies) are bleached with chlorine which creates, among other chemicals, dioxin. Greenpeace has stated that in animal tests 'dioxin was found to be the most potent carcinogen ever discovered'.

According to the US Environmental Agency (EPA) the chlorine used in the bleaching process is also a major source of the dioxin contamination of water. And the dioxin can migrate out of the paper product into the skin, or through teabags and coffee filters into your cup of tea or coffee. So choose unbleached paper products, or use alternatives. Loose tea and coffee, for instance, or a reusable metal filter for coffee; newspaper and old supermarket carrier bags instead of plastic binliners; cotton or linen handkerchiefs instead of paper tissues.

Aluminium foil is also environmentally costly because rainforests are being cut down in order to mine the bauxite ore from which it is made. And aluminium is not a good metal to have in contact with food because it has been linked with Alzheimer's disease. I no longer use aluminium foil for wrapping foods; and it certainly shouldn't get into contact with acidic foods such as citrus fruits or tomatoes because the acid increases the chances of the aluminium leaching out of the foil.

Instead of polythene bags and clingfilm I often find that small, reusable glass and china containers are fine for storing things in the fridge; and it's surprising how often greaseproof paper or plates can be used instead of aluminium foil, to cover large bowls or containers.

Plastics are cheap to produce but they are non-biodegradable so the rubbish just piles up. When we use plastic, we are littering the earth, and even when it's burnt, it gives off dangerous dioxins. I find that I think twice now before I buy or use anything plastic.

There is something extremely satisfying about finding such replacements, and much joy to be had in using natural products. Look in your local Oxfam shop for products from Third World countries, or write for the catalogues (page 229).

Casseroles and tableware

Hand-crafted casseroles, plates and dishes are in keeping with the spirit of Green Age cooking, but make sure that any glazes used are non-toxic. Other useful items include hand-made baskets and table mats, drying-up cloths made from soft cotton or terry towelling, and tablecloths and napkins made from easy-care pure cotton. Wooden bowls and chopping boards are pleasant to use and attractive but do take care not to buy any made from tropical hardwoods, as you will thereby contribute to the destruction of the rainforests. For further information on wood, consult the *Good Wood Guide* (page 229). You might also like to build up a set of pale green glass candlesticks, glasses, bowls, jugs and vases made from recycled glass. These are made by Parlane, available from the Perfect Glass Shop (page 229).

7

Getting Started

It's important to follow your own pace. Some people like to jump straight in, sweep their larder and fridge clean of all non-green products and revolutionize their eating habits from Day 1. If that's your way, excellent. Go on to the section headed 'Simple Changes', then start straight away with the 14-Day Green Age Diet Plan (page 63).

Other people like to move more gently into this diet. If this is you, you have several options. Firstly, you could make some simple changes to your way of eating and cooking, as suggested overleaf. Then, for a week or two, you could have a Green Age breakfast and lunch, and a normal evening meal. Or you could have a few Green Age days each week, gradually increasing the number of days. Or you could try the 14-Day Green Age Diet Plan and then review the situation.

When changing your diet gradually, it's helpful to make a plan so that you move progressively towards an improved, 'greener' way of eating. It's all too easy to make a couple of changes and then get stuck in a rut! If you think you might fall into this trap, you can follow the Eight-Week Plan of Action (page 59) which helps you monitor your progress.

Whether you change quickly or slowly, don't think of the foods you're not eating. Concentrate on the wide range of delicious foods you *can* eat, and choose your favourites. Because this diet is based on good, simple foods like potatoes, pasta, wholewheat bread and fresh fruit and vegetables, most people will find plenty of foods they like.

Simple Changes

These are some of the positive things you can do straight away to make your diet healthier.

- Use olive oil for cooking and salads.
- Use seasonal fresh fruits and vegetables instead of canned or frozen ones.
- Stop buying sugar; use small quantities of raw organic honey, date syrup, rice syrup or real maple syrup and dried fruits instead.
- Change from ordinary table or cooking salt to sea salt and use sparingly.
- Stop buying cakes, biscuits, ice cream and desserts. Replace them with fresh and dried fruits, good wholewheat bread and honey, or home-made wholewheat buns and cakes such as the ones on pages 211–20. (See Ideas for Snacks on page 70.)
- Have at least one of these with every lunch and evening meal: raw or lightly cooked broccoli or Brussels sprouts, leafy green salad, raw carrots, tomatoes, celery sticks.
- Stop cooking in aluminium saucepans. Beg, borrow or buy new enamel-coated or stainless-steel saucepans.
- Buy a water purifier or switch to bottled spring water.
- Discover the pleasure of drinking herb teas, weak normal tea or coffee made from decaffeinated coffee beans, clear, without milk or sugar. (Although it may be difficult at first, after a fortnight you'll never want to have these drinks any other way!)
- Change from cow's milk to soya milk or a home-made nut-milk such as Sunflower Milk (page 112).

The more you can keep to the diet, the better it will work for you. But don't punish yourself. This diet is about celebration, not punishment. It's a celebration of the life-force in natural foods; of the clean, fertile earth; of joy in sharing the earth's foods; and of knowing that your body is as strong and healthy as it can be.

Eight-Week Plan of Action

Tick off the boxes to record your progress as you put the Green Age Diet into practice.

Week 1

Tick when done

- [ ] Start using soya milk instead of dairy milk; try small quantities of different brands until you find your favourite, or make your own (page 109).
- [ ] Use up remaining supplies of butter, then replace with a pure vegetable margarine – read the labels carefully. Vitaquell from the healthfood shop is an excellent one, but, again, experiment with different types to find the one you prefer.
- [ ] Write to Friends of the Earth (page 229) enclosing an SAE to find out where your nearest bottle bank, newspaper and tin collection points are.
- [ ] If you're using aluminium saucepans, window-shop for some healthier alternatives (page 49) and start saving to buy some.
- [ ] Have Green Age breakfasts on every alternate day.

Week 2

☐ When your cooking fats are used up, buy a cheap pure olive oil for cooking.

☐ Make a note to replace washing-up liquid, washing powder and cleaning materials, as they're used up, with 'environment-friendly' ones, such as those made by Ecover.

☐ Continue with the Green Age breakfasts on alternate days, and have two days of Green Age lunches this week, too.

☐ Find suitable places for storing bottles, tins and newspapers, ready for taking to the recycling collection points.

Week 3

☐ Collect together lidded containers for storing food in the refrigerator, to avoid the need for clingfilm or aluminium foil.

☐ Replace supplies of aluminium foil, as they're used up, with greaseproof paper. And buy kitchen roll, paper tissues and loo rolls made from recycled paper. (Enquire about these recycled products at your local supermarket – several chains stock them.)

☐ Have Green Age breakfasts all week and Green Age lunches on three days.

Week 4

☐ Buy canvas or string shopping bags (you can pop the string ones into a handbag or pocket so that they're easily available) to avoid the need for supermarket plastic carriers. Explain to shopkeepers and other shoppers why you are doing this.

☐ How are the Green Age breakfasts and lunches going? Continue with these, and on one of the days, have a Green Age evening meal, to make a complete day of Green Age eating.

☐ Buy, or plan to buy, a jug-type water purifier. Check how many times you need to refill this over several days and make a note of when you will need a new cartridge.

Week 5

☐ Find a healthy substitute for canned or bottled drinks – for instance fruit juices diluted with filtered or spring water, possibly with ice and lemon or lime.

☐ Review your progress on collection of bottles, tins and newspapers for recycling. Are you able to drop these at the collection points on your way somewhere else, without making a special journey?

☐ Think about the beverages you're drinking. Consider tracking down a supply of coffee for which Third World countries receive a fair price. Try Oxfam or Traidcraft (pages 229, 230).

☐ Try a herb tea or weak China or Darjeeling tea without any type of milk – Celestial Seasonings herb teas are my favourites.

☐ Have two days of completely Green Age eating.

Week 6

☐ Check your consumption of fresh, seasonal fruits and vegetables. Are you able to use them frequently in preference to canned and frozen ones? Try to have at least one of these at every meal: a piece of fresh fruit or a glass of freshly squeezed juice; raw or cooked leafy green vegetables; raw carrot, grated or in sticks; raw tomato.

☐ Have three days of completely Green Age meals.

☐ Can you make five to seven lunches Green Age?

Week 7

☐ Continue with your Green Age lunches and breakfasts, and enjoy them. Find your favourites and stick to them, or have fun experimenting.

☐ Can you make every other evening meal Green Age?

Week 8

☐ Review your progress over the past seven weeks and list any goals which you are still working towards. It might be helpful to stick this inside a kitchen cupboard door to remind you.

☐ Have a week of completely Green Age eating.

Congratulations!

8

14-Day Green Age Diet Plan

This is a basic framework which can be varied as you like. The meals can be expanded with soups or other starters and with fresh fruit, or fruit mixtures, for desserts. If you wish to lose weight, follow the diet plan as described but leave out the desserts, oily salad dressings and avocado: these can be added later, once you have reached your perfect weight.

For super-quick weight loss, start off with the Quick-Slim Diet Plan (page 80) which you can follow for as long as you like, before moving on to the standard Green Age Diet.

Breakfast

Breakfast is a feast of grains and fruits, mixed or eaten on their own. Choose from the following:

Fresh fruit
and/or
Fresh fruit juice
or
Mango Whizz (page 110), Energy Fruit Salad (page 113) or any of the other fruit salads and shakes (pages 110–12)
or
Porridge (page 105), Basic Muesli (page 106) or packet muesli, with fresh fruit juice, and Apricot Sauce (page 110), to moisten

or

Wholewheat toast, bread or rolls, topped with low-sugar preserves or marmalade, honey, or a scraping of pure vegetable margarine or unsalted butter

or

If you prefer a cooked breakfast, a vegetarian burger or sausage with fried mushrooms and onions, and grilled tomatoes

or

Mushrooms or grilled tomatoes on wholewheat toast

or

Baked, fried or steamed-in-their-skins potatoes

or

Tofu and Mushroom Scramble (page 176)

and

Tea, coffee or herb tea without sugar or milk, or with a little soya milk (page 109)

If you are slimming, have a piece of fruit or a piece of wholewheat toast with a scraping of butter or pure vegetable margarine.

Lunch

The possibilities include:

More fresh fruit or one of the fruit mixtures (pages 113–14)

or

Any of the salads (pages 120–33) with crusty bread or rolls, perhaps some extra sliced avocado or a Baked Potato (page 161)

or

Pitta Pocket Filled with Sprouted Chick Peas (page 135)

or

A vegetable soup (pages 139–46), some crudités and crusty bread

or

A dip such as Guacamole (page 117) or Hummus (page 118), with some vegetable crudités or wholewheat Melba toast (which is easy to make at home, see page 217)

or

Salad Sandwiches (page 134)

or

Baked Potatoes (page 161) with any of the suggested toppings and/or a large salad (pages 120–33)

or

Spicy Beanburgers (page 173) in a wholewheat burger bun with some salad (pages 120–33)

Evening Meal

When planning main meals, keep them simple. Base them on one or more of the grain and potato group of foods, or the pulse group or the nuts and seeds (see page 21 for these groups), then add a large leafy green salad and/or other fresh seasonal vegetables, either raw or lightly steamed. If you plan your meals on this basis, everything else will fall into place. Look after the starches and salads, and the proteins (and pounds) will look after themselves.

So you might have a Mushroom Risotto (page 183) with a crunchy Green Salad (page 122); a Special Vegetable Stir-Fry (page 150) with Steamed Brown Rice (page 180); Spiced Vegetables (page 156), Dal (page 169) and rice; Spaghetti with Fresh Tomato Sauce (page 188), Green Salad with Avocado (page 122), and crusty bread; Vegetable Hotpot (page 157) and a side salad; Healthy Chips (page 164) with a large Green Salad (page 122) and a grated Carrot Salad (page 123).

Although some people may at first find this an unusual way of eating, the Green Age Diet would be considered completely normal in many countries, countries which happen to be the ones with the lowest rates of cancer and heart disease.

In the Mediterranean, for instance, they rarely put butter on bread. Instead, they eat their bread with a little honey or fruit conserve, or with black olives and salad. Bread is also frequently eaten with another dish and used to mop up the delicious juices. For example a simple meal might be a salad of sun-ripened tomatoes and onions, dressed by pouring a little good olive oil and a squeeze of lemon juice or a drop of wine vinegar over the top, with fresh crusty bread. In Greece or the Middle East they might have some Hummus (page 118) with olives and raw vegetables, and dip the bread into this. In these countries, and in many others, it is normal to make a meal out of vegetables.

Here are some suggestions for evening meals. If you are slimming, have small to moderate portions of everything, except for vinaigrette, avocado, puddings and garlic bread, which would be left out entirely. You can have unlimited amounts of all vegetables except potatoes, which you can have in moderation where they are suggested.

DAY 1

Dal (page 169)
Spiced Vegetables (page 156)
Steamed Brown Rice (page 180)
Tomato and Onion Salad (page 121)
Mango chutney

DAY 2

Mushroom Risotto (page 183)
Green Salad with Avocado (page 122)
Garlic Bread (page 137)
Fresh peaches

DAY 3

Spaghetti with Fresh Tomato Sauce (page 188)
Garlic Bread (page 137) or warm wholewheat stick
Green Salad with Avocado (page 122)

DAY 4

Felafel (page 172)
Hummus (page 118) with black olives and lemon juice
Warm pitta bread
Middle Eastern Broad Beans (page 175)
Salad of quartered tomato, spring onions, carrot sticks, and strips of green pepper
(Serve all these dishes together and dip the felafel, pitta bread and vegetables into the Hummus and broad beans.)

DAY 5

Tomato Soup (page 141)
Nut Roast (page 191)
Savoury Sauce (page 207)
Redcurrant jelly
Lightly cooked Brussels sprouts
Roast potatoes

DAY 6

Green Age Chilli (page 168)
Baked Potatoes (page 161) filled with Creamy Sweetcorn (page 162)
Green Salad (page 122)

DAY 7

Parsnip and Celery Strudel with Pine Nuts (page 198)
Fresh Tomato Sauce (page 210)
Lightly cooked green vegetables
Carrots
Mashed potatoes

DAY 8

Yeast-Dough Pizza (page 194) *or* Quick Bread Pizza (page 196)
Mixed Salad (page 120)
Sliced avocado
Banana and Almond Crumble (page 226)

DAY 9

Lentil Loaf (page 171) *or* Lentil Burgers (page 170)
Savoury Sauce (page 207)
Mint Sauce (page 208) *or* apple sauce
Lightly cooked broccoli

DAY 10

Stir-Fried Chinese Vegetables (page 151)
Spring Rolls (page 199)
Steamed Brown Rice (page 180)

DAY 11

Hummus (page 118) with black olives and warm pitta bread
Ratatouille (page 153)
Herby Brown Rice (page 180) *or* crusty French bread
Green Salad (page 122) *or* steamed French beans

DAY 12

Potato Bake (page 158)
Multicoloured Salad (page 124)
Sliced avocado
Baked Apples (page 226)

DAY 13

Green Pea Soup with Mint (page 140)
Ragout of Mushrooms (page 148) *with* Steamed Brown Rice
(page 180)
Green beans, steamed broccoli *or* Green Salad (page 122)
Fresh fruit

DAY 14

Samosas (page 200) *or* Tomatoes Stuffed with Golden Spiced Potatoes (page 160)
Spicy Brown Rice (page 180) *or* Steamed Brown Rice (page 180)
Dal (page 169) *and/or* Spinach with Cumin Seeds (page 155)
Mango chutney

Ideas for Extra Snacks

—Carrot, cucumber or celery sticks
—Quarters of orange, skin still attached, to suck
—Unsulphured dried apricots
—Slices of apple or other favourite fruits
—Banana pops – chunks of banana frozen on a lolly stick
—Seedless grapes
—Frozen seedless grapes
—Strawberries or cherries
—Dates, perhaps stuffed with a nut to replace the stone
—Dried figs
—Raisins or sultanas
—Pieces of fresh coconut
—Nuts (for children over 5 years)
—A handful of sprouted chick peas, mung beans or lentils
—Home-made oatcakes
—Wholewheat bread and no-sugar-added jam
—Wholewheat currant buns or Iced Buns (page 215)
—Home-made Fruit Cake (page 218)
—Home-made Parkin (page 220)

9

Green Age Meals for One

Many of the Green Age foods are simple and quick to prepare, which makes the diet practical if you're eating on your own. Meals like Baked Potatoes (page 161) and salad, Garlic Mushrooms (page 147) with crusty bread and salad, Mediterranean Brown Rice Salad (page 132), Avocado Vinaigrette Salad (page 127), and some of the spaghetti dishes (pages 187–90) can easily be prepared in single portions.

You can add greater variety to the week's meals if you make up a couple of main dishes, or a soup and a main dish, and keep them in the fridge, to alternate with these quick simple meals.

If you have a freezer, you can be even better organized. For instance, to set yourself up for four weeks, make up four main courses in the quantities given. Then divide them into four portions and freeze them. Serve your main courses with simple vegetables or salads, and on the other three days of the week have quick, easy meals like those described above.

Here are evening meals for four weeks, based on making up and freezing four main-course meals. Choose four from the following, which freeze well, divide them into single portions and freeze:

Mushroom Risotto (page 183)
Nut Roast (page 191) – divides into 6 portions
Lentil Loaf (page 171) – divides into 6 portions
Ratatouille (page 153)

Spiced Vegetables (page 156)
Nut Burgers (page 192)
Felafel (page 172)
Yeast-Dough Pizza (page 194)
Green Age Chilli (page 168)
Dal (page 189)
Fresh Tomato Sauce (page 210) – for quick spaghetti dish
Any of the soups (pages 139–46) for serving with bread or
Garlic Bread (page 137) and some salad

In addition, if you like brown rice with your meals, it might
be worth cooking a batch early in the week and keeping it
covered in the fridge. You can reheat it quickly in a sieve over
a pan of boiling water.

So, if you chose to freeze Mushroom Risotto, Nut Roast,
Spiced Vegetables and Lentil Loaf, one week of your four
might look like this:

DAY 1

Freezer meal: Mushroom Risotto (page 183), Green Salad
(page 122), wholewheat bread

DAY 2

Baked Potato (page 161), large salad of lettuce, grated carrot,
chopped celery and sliced tomato, sprouted beans or seeds if
available

DAY 3

Freezer meal: Lentil Loaf (page 171), chutney or pickle, Green
Salad (page 122) *or* steamed cauliflower or broccoli

DAY 4

Garlic Mushrooms (page 147) with crusty bread, Green Salad
(page 122) *or* Mixed Salad (page 120)

DAY 5

Freezer meal: Spiced Vegetables (page 156), Tomato and
Onion Salad (page 121), Steamed Brown Rice (page 180)

DAY 6

Spaghetti with Avocado (page 189), Green Salad (page 122),
warm wholewheat bread

DAY 7

Freezer meal: Nut Roast (page 191), Mixed Salad (page 120)
or steamed broccoli

For the following three weeks you could repeat the freezer
meals, with different meals – or the same ones – on the days
in between. Other possibilities for quick meals might be Big,
Beautiful Biogenic Salad (page 129), Ragout of Mushrooms
(page 148), Beansprout Stir-Fry (page 149), Special Vegetable
Stir-Fry (page 150), Stir-Fried Chinese Vegetables (page 151),
Hot Stuffed Avocado (page 152), Vegetable Hotpot (page
157), Bircher Potatoes (page 162), Quick Bread Pizza (page
196), Vitamin Salad (page 125), Hummus (page 118) *or*
Guacamole (page 117) with crudités, pitta bread or tortilla
chips.

10

Green Age Dinner Parties

One of the pleasures of the Green Age Diet is telling other people about it and, especially, showing them how good it can be by inviting them to share a Green Age meal. Making a truly delicious meal without any animal products is an exciting challenge, and friends are invariably amazed and delighted by the results.

I particularly like to take an ethnic theme and make a complete meal in the style of a country which naturally cooks in the Green Age way. As well as being undeniably delicious, this underlines the point that animal-free eating is not a weird late twentieth-century idea, but a normal and traditional way of life in many parts of the world.

One of the best countries to turn to for inspiration is India, particularly southern India, which offers a feast of wonderful, tasty dishes. These are particularly suitable for entertaining because they improve if they're made the day before (they reheat very well, covered, in a cool oven, or in a pan on top of the stove, depending on the mixture).

Little hot Samosas (page 200) make a tasty start to the meal, or, for cold weather, Spicy Lentil Soup (page 140), followed by a selection of four or five different spiced vegetable mixtures, with some plain or spiced rice. Try Spiced Vegetables (page 156), Spicy Ratatouille (page 154), Golden Potatoes in Coconut Cream (page 160), Spinach with Cumin Seeds (page 155), and Dal (page 169); one or two salads, such as Carrot and Mustard Seed (page 124), or Tomato and Onion (page

121); and a selection of bought chutneys and pickles such as mango chutney and lime pickle.

To accompany these dishes, serve warm, home-made Chapattis (page 211) or poppadums. I buy the packet poppadum circles and deep-fry them myself. The secret with these is to have the oil hot enough, so that they expand and crispen as soon as they go into the pan, and then to keep them warm in a cool oven once they're fried. They then get beautifully crisp and dry.

To drink with the meal, many people prefer lager; I also like the fruitiness of cider with Indian food, or even a full-bodied red or white table wine. I rarely serve a pudding with this type of meal — just plenty of hot coffee or herb tea — although some sliced, fresh ripe mango would be delicious, or Mango Sorbet (page 223).

Another excellent option is a Middle Eastern style meal, also made up of lots of little dishes: a bowl of Bean Salad with Onions and Herbs (page 130), another of Hummus (page 118), some piping hot Felafel (page 172), some Middle Eastern Broad Beans (page 175), a salad of sliced onions and tomatoes, or perhaps Greek Salad with Avocado (page 128), or Bulgur Wheat Salad (page 130), or Mushrooms à la Grecque (page 148), and perhaps a bowl of hot or cold Ratatouille (page 153). These should all be eaten with lots of warm bread; a good Arab bread, if you can get it, or a mixture of white and brown pitta breads.

While you probably wouldn't want to make a meal like this for one or even two people, it isn't much trouble to feed a family or a crowd in this way, especially if you have some of the dishes already in the freezer. Hummus, felafel, Middle Eastern broad beans, and ratatouille freeze excellently. So does the basic bean salad mixture, leaving you just to add some fresh herbs, garlic and chopped onion.

A platter of fresh dates and figs makes a pleasant dessert, or some squares of halva, which you can get at Middle Eastern shops or some supermarkets, or some Turkish Delight (choose one that is made without gelatine). And lots of black coffee or herb tea.

A Chinese meal is another popular choice. Freshly made Spring Rolls (page 199), straight from the oven, make a good start, or clear Oriental Broth (page 146). After this, you could serve Stir-Fried Chinese Vegetables (page 151), plenty of rice (perhaps a choice of white and brown), another dish such as Tofu and Tamari (page 176), and/or an Oriental-style salad, such as Radish, Cucumber and Hiziki (page 126).

Some lychees, either fresh or canned, perhaps with some sliced kiwi fruit and mandarin oranges make a dessert in keeping with the theme. To drink, light white wine, or sake (a Japanese rice liquor usually served warm); and lots of jasmine tea to end.

An Italian meal isn't as unusual, but is also good. Tomato-Cucumber-Avocado Salad (page 127) – the Green Age version of Insalata Tricolore – makes a satisfying first course, especially when served with piping hot Garlic Bread (page 137). Follow this with several types of pasta – pasta mista – either served on one large platter or on separate ones.

Choose different colours and types of pasta, and contrasting sauces; green tagliatelle with Red Pepper Sauce (page 187), Spaghetti with Pesto (page 188), rigatone or penne with Fresh Tomato Sauce (page 210), Fettucine with Creamy Mushroom Sauce (page 190). A salad of radicchio, lettuce, tomato and onion goes well with this, with a good dressing. And a sorbet or ice, Peaches in White Wine (page 225), or just plenty of coffee, to end.

Of course you can also create an excellent Green Age meal without keeping to an ethnic theme. Possible first courses include Green Pea Soup with Mint (page 140), Tomatoes Stuffed with Golden Spiced Potatoes (page 160), or Garlic Mushrooms (page 147) with warm crusty bread. Follow these with Parsnip and Celery Strudel with Pine Nuts (page 198) and a Fresh Tomato Sauce (page 210), or even a good Nut Roast (page 191) with a Wine Sauce (page 208), or Hot Stuffed

Avocado (page 152) which all make good main courses. Peaches in White Wine (page 225), Pears in Red Wine (page 225), or Fruit Platter with Mango Sauce (page 114), could end the meal.

11

The Green Age Diet Out and About

Green Age eating is becoming easier all the time. Many restaurants now offer at least one vegetarian dish which may or may not contain dairy produce. It isn't quite as easy, yet, to get pure vegetarian or vegan meals, although the situation is improving and will continue to do so if restaurants realize the demand is there. So if this is what you want, do make your needs known.

Vegetarian and wholefood restaurants generally offer a good choice of both vegetarian and vegan dishes and at lunchtime they usually provide a good-sized salad or bowl of home-made soup if you want something simple.

Jacket potatoes (ask for them without butter or cheese, as I do, if that is your preference), rolls and salads are widely available at pubs and restaurants for quick lunches, although I wish pubs would serve larger salads and smaller portions of cheese in their ploughman's lunches. I generally ask for a ploughman's with a double portion of salad and no cheese or butter. At sandwich bars where they make up sandwiches to order you can ask them to leave out the butter. A tomato and onion sandwich, a crusty piece of French bread filled with salad, or a salad and avocado sandwich are favourites of mine.

Business lunches can be more of a challenge. If I'm entertaining meat-eaters, I choose a restaurant which I know will have dishes we can all eat and tell them that although I'll be eating vegetarian, I certainly don't expect them to feel they have to do the same. If I'm invited out, I just say (when they invite me) that I'm vegetarian but that I'm always quite happy with a salad or platter of steamed vegetables – which is true!

Ethnic restaurants can be a very good bet for vegetarians and vegans since there are usually several suitable dishes on the menu. Indian restaurants are particularly good, with a range of deliciously spicy dishes to try or, often, a vegetarian thali (a balanced assortment of dishes in small portions). Many Chinese, Thai, Japanese and Middle Eastern restaurants also offer a good choice and a tasty meal.

At Italian restaurants there is usually at least one pasta dish without cheese, or they will prepare pasta with olive oil and garlic if you ask. They may also make up a pizza with extra vegetable topping instead of cheese. If you are really stuck at a restaurant, it is nearly always possible to choose both a first course and a main course from the starters, or just to have a large salad as a main course or a platter of vegetables prepared without butter and cheese – some lemon juice and freshly ground black pepper, or vinaigrette, is nice on these.

Going further afield, airlines will provide a vegetarian or vegan meal on request. Ask about this when you book the flight: some airlines make a note of it then, others like you to phone 24 – 48 hours in advance, so check on their system when booking. If you prefer, you can take your own fruit, mineral water or filtered water (plus ice, in a thermos, if you like), wholewheat crispbread, nuts and raisins, carrot and celery sticks – whatever you fancy – and be self-sufficient.

When you're out and about without food and want a quick healthy Green Age snack, emergency rations available at most places are fresh fruit, crispbread, rolls, nuts and raisins.

Eating out, or eating on the move, are easier to manage than having a meal with friends. Again, it's important to tell them that you're vegetarian or vegan when they ask you, and I always add that I am very happy just to have extra vegetables. I have always found friends very hospitable and helpful over this, although they may need some ideas and suggestions for recipes without dairy produce.

12

Quick-Slim Diet Plan

The slimming version of the 14-Day Green Age Diet results in a good, steady weight-loss of 1 – 1.5 kg (2 – 3 lb) a week. This Quick-Slim Diet is a stricter version for when you want to lose weight faster than this, or to get off to a good start before you move on to the standard 14-Day Green Age Diet. It is the diet which I personally use when I want to lose weight.

I know there are plenty of good reasons for slimming slowly, and I am not in favour of unnatural 'crash' diets. But I'm an impatient person, and I get bored with diets which go on and on slowly and 'sensibly', and I start eating too much again and put the weight back on in a fraction of the time it took to take off. I lost a stone in a fortnight on the Quick-Slim Diet, didn't 'bloat' in the second half of the month as usual, and felt full of energy and wonderful in every way.

This Quick-Slim Diet does not try to make the food too tempting. You eat food in its natural form without any salt. Not eating any salt has, in my experience, a remarkable way of speeding up weight-loss, and it helped me to break my addiction to this seasoning. Eating simple food has the additional advantage of keeping you out of the kitchen, away from temptation. And, to some extent, it lessens your appetite.

The inspiration for the Quick-Slim Diet comes from the Rice Diet, which was developed by Dr Walter Kempner 50 years ago, not, originally, as a slimming diet, but as a treatment for people who were gravely ill with diseases of the heart and circulatory system, and diabetes. Patients put on this diet recovered miraculously. The fact that they also lost weight was a helpful side-effect, although once Dr Kempner's work became known, people came to him specifically to lose weight. Often they were grossly obese, and they would stay on the diet for many months, with increasingly beneficial results. Children, too, thrive on this diet.

The theory behind Dr Kempner's diet was the same as that behind the Green Age Diet. He realized that animal products, with their high proportion of protein and fat, were not the right food for the human body. And he also believed that the body's main need was for complex carbohydrates, with low protein and minimal amounts of fat. Dr Kempner's diet has been described fully and most helpfully in *The Rice Diet Report*, by Judy Moscovitz, which I warmly recommend. The following Quick-Slim Diet is a simple adaptation which I have evolved from my own experience.

Choosing your Goal Weight

The following chart gives the goal weights which Dr Kempner recommends. They are a good deal stricter than those given in most height-weight charts, and make no allowance for 'small', 'medium' or 'large' bones, which he says are confusing and largely irrelevant. He maintains that the important thing is to get rid of all excess fat. Unless you do this, the fat remaining just attracts more fat back again, rather like a tumour which grows again unless it is completely removed. He adds that if you reach your goal weight and then stay there for two years, you need never fear putting the fat back on again. Where you decide to stop is up to you. These weights are very low, and I have never yet reached my own goal weight, but they show how low you can go and, indeed, what Dr Kempner considers best for optimum health.

GOAL WEIGHTS

Women

Height Feet & inches	Weight (no clothes) Pounds	Stones & pounds
4'11"	86	6st 2lb
5'0"	88	6st 4lb
5'1"	90	6st 6lb
5' 2"	92	6st 8lb
5' 3"	100	7st 2lb
5' 4"	102	7st 4lb
5' 5"	105	7st 7lb
5' 6"	113	8st 1lb
5' 7"	116	8st 4lb
5' 8"	120	8st 8lb
5' 9"	127	9st 1lb
5' 10"	131	9st 5lb
5' 11"	134	9st 8lb
6' 0"	141	10st 1lb

For heights in between those given, add 1lb for every ½ inch.

Men

Height Feet & inches	Weight (no clothes) Pounds	Stones & pounds
5'2"	103	7st 5lb
5'3"	107	7st 9lb
5'4"	114	8st 2lb
5' 5"	118	8st 6lb
5' 6"	121	8st 9lb
5' 7"	129	9st 3lb
5' 8"	132	9st 6lb
5' 9"	140	10st
5' 10"	144	10st 4lb
5' 11"	147	10st 7lb
6' 0"	155	11st 1lb
6' 1"	158	11st 4lb
6' 2"	162	11st 8lb
6' 3"	169	12st 1lb
6' 4"	173	12st 5lb
6' 5"	177	12st 9lb

For heights in between those given, add 1¼lb for every ½ inch.

Adapted from the height-weight recommendations given in *The Rice Diet* by Judy Moscovitz.

Recording your Weight-Loss

I like to record my weight-loss on a graph, because it's so heartening to see the line going down and down towards my goal weight. To make a graph, either buy some graph paper and fill it in like the example on page 86 or use the blank graph chart overleaf, filling it in appropriately for your own goal weight. If you have a great deal of weight to lose, it's a good idea to set some intermediate goals on the way to your ultimate goal.

When you are recording your weight, you may find that you reach a plateau and stick there for several days. Don't let this discourage you – it often happens on a diet – just persevere. In a day or two you'll start to lose again, and may even suddenly drop by several pounds. Women may find that they plateau for a few days, or even go up a pound or two just before a period. But as this diet is so low in salt this happens less on the Quick-Slim Diet than on others.

QUICK-SLIM PROGRESS CHART

You may want to photocopy the chart rather than spoil your book. I've done two charts for 4 weeks each, but you may want to do 8 weeks at once. Fill in your target weight (or your first target if you have more than 2½ stone to lose). Number pounds, or stones and pounds, from just below your target weight, up the left-hand side of the chart. Use a dot to record your first day's weight. The next day, weigh yourself again and record your weight by drawing a dot on the line for 'Day 2'. Then join up the dots. Continue like this until you reach your target weight.

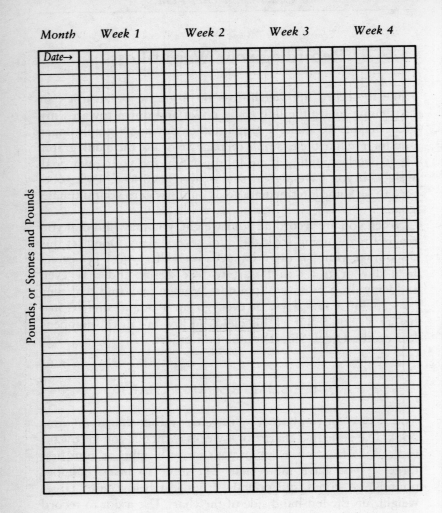

Month   Week 1   Week 2   Week 3   Week 4

Date→

Pounds, or Stones and Pounds

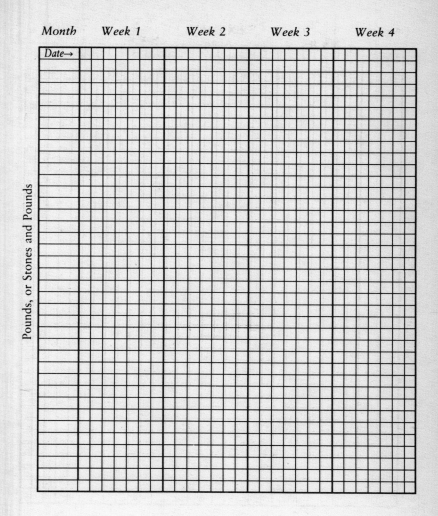

Month   Week 1   Week 2   Week 3   Week 4

Date→

Pounds, or Stones and Pounds

EXAMPLE
August

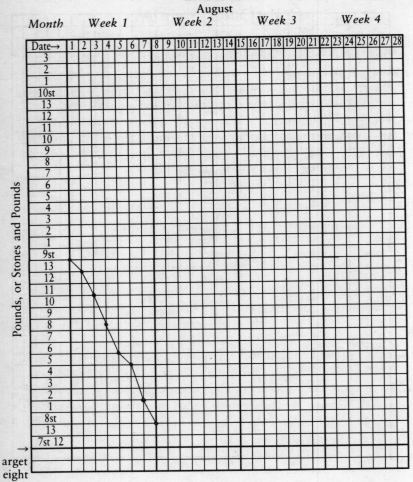

86

The Quick-Slim Diet

This begins with a cleansing diet, which can continue for a week, a fortnight, or as long as you are feeling good on it and getting worthwhile results. Some of Dr Kempner's grossly overweight patients stayed on this diet for months, with great benefit to their general health as well as consistent weight-loss. After this cleansing period, you can move on to the ongoing diet (page 90), in which vegetables, pasta, potatoes, grains, bread, fresh herbs and spices are included.

1 The Preliminary Cleansing Diet

During the day you can have 7 items consisting of:

1 piece of fruit for breakfast;
2 pieces of fruit and a 100 g (4 oz) serving of cooked rice (white or brown, without any salt), or a shredded wheat, for lunch and the same for the evening meal.
No salt, milk, sugar or flavourings except for fresh (not bottled) lemon juice, and a non-sodium sweetener if liked.
To drink, you can have filtered or spring water on its own, or with lemon or lime juice and non-sodium sweetener; decaffeinated coffee and regular or herb teas, without milk.

A piece of fruit is:

an apple, banana, pear, mango, wedge of melon, half a grapefruit, peach, nectarine, or the equivalent in smaller fruits, such as 3 fresh apricots, 2 figs, 4 prunes, or 225 g (8 oz) soft fruits such as cherries, strawberries, raspberries, blueberries, blackberries, unsweetened fruit salad, unsweetened apple sauce, 40 g (1½ oz) raisins or sultanas (no dates allowed), a 200 ml (7 fl oz) glass of unsweetened fruit juice. Unsweetened canned fruits may also be used: 225 g (8 oz), with 2 table-spoons of juice, counts as 'a piece of fruit'.

Choose your favourite fruits and try different types of rice — brown long-grain, brown basmati, white long-grain, white basmati (but not wild rice, which isn't a grain). Cook up a batch of rice and keep it in the fridge ready. Have it hot or cold, mixed with all or some of your fruit, plain, or whizzed with the fruit and frozen to make an 'ice'.

Here are some examples of Preliminary Cleansing Diet meals which worked for me, but the idea is to discover and enjoy your own combinations.

DAY 1

Breakfast

225 g (8 oz) ripe black cherries

Lunch

1 very large ripe mango (I counted this as 2 'pieces of fruit' as it was so big)
100 g (4 oz) white long-grain rice

Evening Meal

225 g (8 oz) ripe black cherries
1 large banana
100 g (4 oz) white long-grain rice

DAY 2

Breakfast

skipped (if you skip a meal during this fruit and rice phase of the diet you don't make it up later — this helps to break your attachment to food)

Lunch

1 large apple, chopped and mixed with 100 g (4 oz) white long-grain rice and 40 g (1 ½ oz) raisins

Evening Meal

1 shredded wheat crumbled up, mixed with a juicy chopped orange and 40 g (1 ½ oz) raisins, left to soak for several hours.

DAY 3

Breakfast

1 banana

Lunch

1 wedge melon
100 g (4 oz) brown rice
225 g (8 oz) strawberries

Evening Meal

100 g (4 oz) brown rice mixed with 20 g (¾ oz) raisins (½ serving)
1 large cooking apple stuffed with 20 g (¾ oz) raisins (½ serving), scored lightly around the middle and baked

I did the Preliminary Cleansing Diet for a fortnight and thought it would be monotonous, but I actually found it fun, rewarding and carefree. I did it in the summer and enjoyed trying all the different summer fruits which were around, although it would be pleasant in the winter, too, with grapes, satsumas and muscatel raisins. I often chopped up the fruit, put it in a bowl with the cold rice and ate it with chopsticks. Occasionally I crumbled up the shredded wheat and mixed it with a serving of raisins and chopped-up orange or banana, then left it for several hours, so that it made a kind of cake, which I enjoyed for a change. I often packed up my portion of fruit and rice and ate it outside in the sunshine, or took out some shredded wheat with me and ate it with fresh, summer fruit which I bought at a fruit stall.

Sometimes I felt a bit hungry in the late afternoon or evening, but I found that a cup of tea or decaffeinated coffee, plus something pleasant to do, like listening to some favourite music, reading an entertaining book, taking a bath with scented oils, phoning a friend, planning what new clothes I was going to buy once I'd reached my target weight, or, if the worst came to the worst, going to bed early, worked wonders. Certainly, stepping on the scales each morning and finding I'd lost yet another pound, or two, or three, made it all more than worthwhile.

2 The Ongoing Diet

The structure of the diet remains the same in that it is based on 7 items or 'servings', 1 for breakfast and 3 each for lunch and the evening meal, but these 7 items can now be chosen freely from fruits, vegetables, grains, potatoes and pulses.

Each of these counts as 1 serving:

90

100 g (4 oz) cooked rice, any type
1 medium-sized potato, baked or boiled
1 corn on the cob
90 g (3½ oz) cooked pasta
25 g (1 oz) rolled oats (not 'instant')
'a piece of fruit' (as listed on page 87)
2 tomatoes, or a tomato salad made from 2 tomatoes and
  ¼ – ½ sliced onion
tomato sauce, made by heating above ingredients in a pan
  without oil or seasonings until puréed
15 – 20 spears asparagus
225 – 350 g (8 – 12 oz) any vegetables, except starchy ones
  (such as peas, sweetcorn, water chestnuts, okra, broad beans)
2 peppers
120 – 165 g (4½ – 5½ oz) peas, sweetcorn, water chestnuts,
  okra, broad beans
100 – 175 g (4 – 6 oz) tofu
50 – 75 g (2 – 3 oz) uncooked lentils or beans (175 – 225 g (6 –
  8 oz) cooked weight)
1 slice of bread or a roll, both preferably salt-free

You can follow the diet exactly as it is given, or you can use
the principles to include your own favourite foods from those
available. It's best to come out of the fruit and rice cleansing
phase gently by gradually introducing other foods. Keep to
your 7 servings, and, at first, it is best to continue with a piece
of fruit for breakfast. However lunch and the evening meal can
be made up of whatever 3 items you fancy.

You can also mix servings, to give more variety. So, for
instance, you might have 1 pepper (½ serving) stuffed with
your full quota of rice, which has been mixed with 20 g (¾ oz)
raisins (½ serving), and served with 175 g (6 oz) mixed green
salad vegetables (another ½ serving). You could round off the
meal with 100 g (4 oz) cherries (another ½ serving).

If you start introducing these other food options gradually,
this structuring becomes automatic. You will find that you are

beginning to think in terms of a little of lots of different foods, as a naturally slim person does, instead of in large, undisciplined quantities.

Remember, no salt, no milk, and keep to the drinks allowed in the Preliminary Cleansing Diet (page 87). You may have an occasional glass of dry wine in place of 1 serving, but I would suggest that you only allow yourself this if you're quite sure your willpower won't slip as a result, and keep to one normal-sized wineglassful. This represents about the same number of calories as a banana.

You can use fresh chopped herbs, fresh crushed garlic, fresh grated ginger, freshly ground black pepper, dry mustard, grated nutmeg, rice vinegar, and of course lemon juice, to flavour. The Japanese Dressing (page 116), made without salt, can be used over salads, so you might like to make up a jar of this and keep it in the fridge. Remember, though, the simpler you keep this diet, the better it will work, and the quicker you'll reach your goal weight.

You can repeat this Ongoing Diet for any length of time, or you can repeat individual days of it. If you wish, you can also include days of just rice and fruit, to cleanse your system, and speed up your weight-loss.

Here are some suggested menus for the first 14 days of your Ongoing Diet. As with the Preliminary Cleansing Diet, you should feel free to experiment with your 7 servings and find the combinations that suit you best.

DAY 1

Breakfast

Cox apple *or* other piece of fruit of your choice

Lunch

Fruit and rice salad: 100 g (4 oz) cooked rice mixed with 20 g (¾ oz) raisins or sultanas (soaked in hot water for 10 minutes, to 'plump'), 50 g (2 oz) sliced grapes, and ½ sliced banana

Evening Meal

100 g (4 oz) hot, cooked rice sprinkled with 20 g (¾ oz) raisins or sultanas
Tomato salad: 2 tomatoes and ½ onion, sliced
100 g (4 oz) fruit (e.g. ½ banana left over from lunch or cherries, raspberries or strawberries) *or* leave out the raisins or sultanas and have 225 g (8 oz) fresh fruit

DAY 2

Breakfast

225 g (8 oz) cherries *or* other piece of fruit of your choice

Lunch

Mediterranean salad: 100 g (4 oz) cooked brown or white rice mixed with 2 chopped tomatoes, and ¼ onion and ¼ green pepper, both chopped. Season with lemon juice and freshly ground black pepper
1 serving fresh strawberries or grapes

Evening Meal

Paella: heat 2 chopped, skinned tomatoes, ¼ onion and ¼ green pepper in a saucepan until soft, then add 100 g (4 oz) cooked rice. Season with lemon juice and freshly ground black pepper
1 wedge orange melon

DAY 3

Breakfast

Ripe juicy pear *or* other piece of fruit of your choice

Lunch

Fruit and rice salad (see Day 1), or Mediterranean salad (see Day 2), followed by a piece of fruit
or
100 g (4 oz) brown rice
15 – 20 asparagus spears with freshly squeezed lemon juice and crushed garlic
1 glass dry white wine *or* 225 g (8 oz) strawberries

Evening meal

1 wedge melon
Beefsteak tomato, hollowed out, stuffed with chopped tomato centre mixed with 100g (4oz) cooked rice and 2 tablespoons raisins, baked for about 15 minutes until heated through. Serve with cooked broccoli, brussel sprouts, spinach *or* a green salad

DAY 4

Breakfast

1 wedge melon *or* other fresh fruit of your choice

Lunch

Large rice salad: 100 g (4 oz) steamed brown rice mixed with 225 – 350 g (8 – 12 oz) vegetables, including grated carrot, chopped tomato, chopped lettuce or whatever you fancy, dressed with rice vinegar

225 g (8 oz) cherries, *or* you can sprinkle the salad with 40 g (1½ oz) sultanas or raisins instead

Evening meal

Stuffed green pepper: wash, halve and de-seed pepper, then boil until only just tender. Drain and fill halves with mixture of 1 chopped tomato, ¼ chopped onion, 4 – 5 sliced button mushrooms, and 100 g (4 oz) cooked rice. Then bake in the oven at 200°C/400°F/Gas Mark 6 until heated through.
Serve with a salad made from a wonderful mixture of leafy green vegetables and some chopped fresh herbs if available, *or* follow with 225 g (8 oz) fresh fruit salad, perhaps including orange segments, sliced kiwi fruit and strawberries

DAY 5

Breakfast

½ grapefruit *or* other piece of fresh fruit of your choice

Lunch

Mediterranean salad (see Day 2) and a piece of fruit, *or* fruit and rice salad (see Day 1), *or* 100 g (4 oz) cooked rice and a tomato salad (see Day 1) and a piece of fruit

Evening Meal

90 g (3½ oz) spaghetti served with a tomato sauce: heat 2 chopped, skinned tomatoes, and ¼ onion and ¼ green pepper, both chopped in a saucepan until soft
Large green salad including as many different types of leafy green vegetable as you can, and some fresh chopped mint or other herbs
or a piece of fresh fruit of your choice

DAY 6

Breakfast

1 large ripe peach *or* other fresh fruit of your choice

Lunch

Wholewheat roll filled with sliced tomato, lettuce and onion, served with extra salad
a piece of fresh fruit of your choice

Evening Meal

Steamed Chinese-style vegetables: a few baby sweetcorn, beansprouts, sliced mushrooms, diagonally sliced carrots, bamboo shoots and a few water chestnuts
100 g (4 oz) cooked rice
a glass of dry wine *or* piece of fruit of your choice

DAY 7

Breakfast

1 banana *or* piece of fruit of your choice

Lunch

Cooked corn on the cob (no butter, oil or salt, of course)
Crunchy salad: fingers of raw carrot, celery sticks, strips of green pepper, cucumber, spring onion, and Japanese dressing (page 116) if liked
a piece of fresh fruit of your choice

Evening Meal

Steamed vegetable platter: your favourite vegetables, with 100 g (4 oz) steamed new potatoes, sprinkled with lemon juice, freshly ground black pepper and chopped fresh mint, parsley or dill
Have this with tomato sauce (see Day 5), *or* a glass of wine, *or* a piece of fruit

DAY 8

Breakfast

225 g (8 oz) mixed fresh fruit salad: perhaps orange and grapefruit; or pear, strawberry and banana; or apricot and kiwi fruit; *or* a piece of fresh fruit of your choice

Lunch

A medium-sized baked potato filled with 100 g (4 oz) drained canned or cooked frozen sweetcorn, mashed a bit to 'cream' it, if liked
Mixed salad: grated carrot, tomato, lettuce, cucumber, or whatever else you fancy, lemon juice or Japanese Dressing (page 116)

Evening Meal ·

Ratatouille: heat together, in a lidded saucepan, 2 skinned tomatoes, ¼ chopped onion, ½ chopped green pepper, 175 g (6 oz) chopped courgettes and 175 g (6 oz) chopped aubergines, for about 30 minutes, or until tender. Season with crushed garlic, lemon juice and chopped parsley
Medium-sized baked potato, 100 g (4 oz) steamed new potatoes, *or* 100 g (4 oz) boiled rice

DAY 9

Breakfast

3 ripe apricots or other fresh fruit of your choice

Lunch

Complete-meal muesli: 20 g (¾ oz) rolled oats moistened with filtered or spring water, with 40 g (1½ oz) raisins and 1 sliced banana

Evening Meal

Mexican rice: heat together in a saucepan until tender 100 g (4 oz) drained canned or cooked frozen sweetcorn, ½ chopped green pepper, ¼ chopped onion, a small sliced courgette, and 1 skinned and chopped tomato. Then add 100 g (4 oz) hot, cooked rice

DAY 10

Breakfast

1 medium-sized ripe juicy mango *or* other fresh fruit of your choice

Lunch

100 g (4 oz) steamed new potatoes
Large salad made from crisp lettuce, grated carrot, sliced tomato and chopped celery
a piece of fresh fruit

Evening Meal

100 g (4 oz) Mushroom Risotto (page 183): make as described but cook the tomato and onion in the pan gently without oil, and don't add salt
Mixed Salad (page 120), with Japanese Dressing (page 116)

DAY 11

Breakfast

Mango Whizz (page 110), *or* other fresh fruit of your choice

Lunch

Green Soup (page 142)
1 slice wholewheat toast or a crusty roll
Crudités: a few cherry tomatoes, florets of cauliflower, sticks of carrot, celery sticks, *or* a piece of fresh fruit of your choice

Evening Meal

Red bean chilli: made by heating together, in a lidded saucepan, 2 skinned tomatoes, ¼ onion, 1 grated carrot and ½ green pepper, for about 10 minutes, then adding 100 g (4 oz) cooked drained red kidney beans, 1 crushed garlic clove and a good pinch of chilli powder. Cook for about 10 minutes, until all the vegetables are tender. Flavour with a little lemon juice, and serve with a green salad.

DAY 12

Breakfast

200 ml (7 fl oz) freshly squeezed orange juice, *or* piece of fresh fruit of your choice

Lunch

Mushrooms on toast: 225 g (8 oz) button mushrooms, sliced and simmered in water, drained, sprinkled with chopped parsley and grated nutmeg, and served on 1 slice wholewheat toast
Large chopped lettuce and tomato salad with lemon juice or Japanese Dressing (page 116)

Evening Meal

Vegetable stew: simmer together in a saucepan for about 20 minutes until tender 2 skinned and chopped tomatoes, ¼ chopped onion, ¼ chopped green pepper, 1 sliced courgette, 1 diced carrot, 1 stick chopped celery, 100 g (4 oz) sliced mushrooms, and a few green beans
100 g (4 oz) cooked rice, *or* 100 g (4 oz) steamed new potatoes, *or* green salad, *or* a glass of dry wine, *or* a piece of fruit of your choice

DAY 13

Breakfast

1 banana, *or* other fresh fruit of your choice

Lunch

A medium-sized baked potato with a squeeze of lemon juice and some freshly ground black pepper
Mixed salad: grated carrot, tomato, lettuce, cucumber, or whatever else you fancy, lemon juice or Japanese Dressing (page 116)

Evening Meal

Red cabbage casserole: simmer together gently in a lidded pan for about 45 minutes, or until tender, 350 g (12 oz) shredded red cabbage, ½ chopped dessert apple, 20 g (¾ oz) raisins or sultanas and ½ chopped onion. Flavour with lemon juice or rice vinegar, freshly ground black pepper and grated nutmeg or powdered cinnamon
A medium-sized baked potato

DAY 14

Breakfast

4 prunes, soaked *or* dry, or fresh fruit of your choice

Lunch

Mediterranean salad (see Day 2)

Evening Meal

175 g (6 oz) slice Lentil Loaf (page 171) (blot well to remove oil), served with mint sauce made by adding chopped mint to rice vinegar
100 g (4 oz) steamed new potatoes in their skins
225 g (8 oz) cauliflower florets

3 Coming Off the Diet, and Maintenance

You can repeat this Ongoing Diet for as long as you like, varying it as suggested to include the permitted foods which you like best. You will come to love it and find that it has many advantages. (It has helped me in re-educating my palate to like food without lashings of salt.) It certainly allows you to appreciate how good simple foods like rice and fruit can be, without any additional flavourings. The 7-servings-a-day programme provides a simple structure, and means you can eat a large variety of foods, yet still lose weight quickly and reliably without ever having to think about counting calories.

When you have been on the diet for a while, lost some weight and gained more control over your eating, you can begin distributing your 7 food items as you like throughout the day. For instance, you might prefer not to have breakfast, but to have lunch made up of 3 items, and dinner of 4 items, using your breakfast serving there. Or you might prefer to have a light lunch, and 5 items in the evening. You can also have items other than fruit for breakfast, such as a piece of wholewheat toast with up to 2 teaspoons of clear honey or sugarless spread which you can now include as a 'free' bonus item each day.

As you near your goal weight you can introduce more dishes from the recipe section of this book, using the minimum of oil and no salt when making them. Or you can move on to the slimming version of the 14-Day Green Age Diet Plan. Alternatively, you could have Green Age recipes on some days and stricter, Quick-Slim menus on other days.

If you follow this Quick-Slim Diet, as described, I think you will be thrilled with the results and you will look and feel better than ever. So good luck – and keep going!

PART TWO

The Recipes

1

Breakfast

Porridge

A healthy, simple and warming breakfast, porridge can be made by the traditional method with oatmeal, or, more quickly, with rolled oats, one of the least processed breakfast cereals. As well as making a delicious start to the day, oats (or rather the soluble fibre they contain) are thought to be very helpful in lowering blood cholesterol.

Traditional Method   Serves 2

Bring 600 ml (1 pint) of water to the boil in a medium-sized saucepan. Gradually whisk in 50 g (2 oz) medium oatmeal. Continue to whisk until the mixture comes back to the boil, then cover and cook over a very gentle heat for 25–30 minutes, stirring from time to time.

Quick Method   Serves 2

Put 50 g (2 oz) rolled oats (or oats up to the 150 ml (5 fl oz) mark on a measuring cup) into a medium-sized saucepan. Add 300 ml (10 fl oz) water, and stir over a moderate heat for about 2 minutes, until thickened. If the porridge is too thick, add more water, stirring well.

TOPPINGS FOR PORRIDGE

—Soya Milk (page 109), Coconut Cream (page 109) or Nut Cream (page 108)
—A few raisins, sultanas, chopped dates or dried apricots
—Reduced-sugar preserves
—Real maple syrup
—Date syrup
—Clear honey
—Real Barbados sugar
—Chopped or grated nuts
—Sliced banana
—A sprinkling of ground ginger, powdered cinnamon or grated nutmeg

Basic Muesli   *Makes 7–8 servings*

If you like home-made muesli, it can save time to make up a supply in bulk. Here's a basic recipe; the ingredients can be varied.

225 g (8 oz) rolled oats
100 g (4 oz) raisins
100 g (4 oz) mixed chopped brazil nuts and sunflower seeds

Put all the ingredients into a bowl and mix. Store in an airtight container. To use, simply add Soya Milk (page 109), fruit juice or water to the required amount. You can eat it as it is, or add any other ingredients you fancy: chopped fresh or dried (raw or soaked and cooked) apricots, peaches, pears, figs or dates; wheatgerm, pumpkin seeds, shredded coconut, honey or Barbados sugar

Creamy Oats   *Serves 1*

25 g (1 oz) rolled oats
water
1 – 2 tablespoons raisins or sultanas
1 banana or sweet pear, peeled and chopped

Put the oats into a bowl, cover with water and leave to soak
for at least 30 minutes. If you like the raisins or sultanas plump
and juicy, add these to the mixture with the water. Just before
serving, add the banana or pear.

2

Nut Milks, Creams,
Sweet Sauces and Drinks

Nut Milk *Makes 300−450 ml (10−15 fl oz)*

50 g (2 oz) cashew nuts or blanched almonds
200−300 ml (7−10 fl oz) filtered or spring water

Put the nuts and water into the liquidizer or food processor
and whizz until smooth. For a thicker, creamier version, use
less water.

Nut Cream *Makes 250−300 ml (8−10 fl oz)*

100 g (4 oz) cashew nuts or blanched almonds
150 ml (5 fl oz) filtered or spring water
a little clear honey
a small piece of vanilla pod or a few drops of real vanilla
essence

Put the nuts, water and honey into the liquidizer or food
processor and whizz until smooth and creamy. If you're using
the vanilla pod, your cream will have some black specks in it,
but will taste superb. (Any larger pieces of vanilla pod which
don't get broken down by the blender can be removed and
used again.) If you prefer a thinner cream, add more water.

Coconut Cream   *Makes 150 ml (5 fl oz)*

This makes a delicious, creamy topping for pouring over fresh fruit. It's particularly good with strawberries.

75 g (3 oz) creamed coconut
150 ml (5 fl oz) boiling water

Cut the creamed coconut into small pieces and put into a bowl or jug. Add the boiling water and stir until the coconut has dissolved. Leave to get cold, then whisk lightly with a fork.

Soya Milk   *Makes about 1.2 litres (2 pints)*

Although you can buy good soya milk, you can also make an excellent one at home.

225 g (8 oz) soya beans
filtered water
1 vanilla pod
1 tablespoon pure, lightly flavoured olive oil
a dash of honey

Soak the beans in plenty of filtered water for 2 days, changing the water twice a day. Liquidize the beans with 1.5 litres (2½ pints) filtered water. Then pour the mixture through a sieve lined with a piece of muslin, squeezing through as much liquid as possible into a large saucepan. Add the vanilla pod. Bring to the boil, then remove the vanilla pod and liquidize again with the oil, and a dash of honey to taste. Strain through muslin again. (The vanilla pod can be washed, dried and used a number of times.)

Apricot Sauce   *Makes 350 – 450 ml (12 – 15 fl oz)*

50 g (2 oz) Hunza apricots, or other unsulphured dried apricots
300 ml (10 fl oz) filtered or spring water

Soak the apricots in the water overnight. The next day, remove
the stones if necessary, and put the apricots into a food
processor or liquidizer with their soaking water. Whizz until
smooth.

Mango Whizz   *Makes 1 large or 2 small glasses*

1 ripe mango, peeled, halved, stoned and cut into chunks
a little filtered or spring water

Put the mango into a liquidizer or food processor with the
water and whizz to a purée. Add more water to thin until you
have a drinkable consistency. Serve in a tall glass.

Strawberry and
Almond Shake   *Makes 1 large or 2 small glasses*

For a delicious, thick, chilled version of this, put the
strawberries in the freezer for 1 – 2 hours before making the
shake.

4 – 6 ripe strawberries, fresh, or frozen (as described above)
200 ml (7 fl oz) home-made Nut Milk (page 108)

Put the strawberries into the liquidizer with the almond milk
and whizz until thick and smooth. Thin with a little spring or
filtered water as necessary.

Banana Shake   *Makes 1 large glass*

For a delicious, thick, chilled version of this, and of the other banana drinks which follow, cut the banana into chunks and place in the freezer for several hours until firm.

1 banana, peeled and cut into chunks, fresh, or frozen (as described above)
200 ml (7 fl oz) freshly squeezed orange juice or home-made Nut Milk (page 108)

Put the banana into the liquidizer with the orange juice or nut milk and whizz until thick and smooth.

Banana-Berry Shake   *Makes 1 large glass*

1 banana, peeled and cut into chunks, fresh, or frozen (as described above)
100 – 225 g (4 – 8 oz) strawberries or raspberries, washed
200 ml (7 fl oz) freshly squeezed orange juice

Liquidize the fruit and juice until thick and smooth.

Banana-Tahini Shake   *Makes 1 large glass*

1 banana, peeled and cut into chunks, fresh, or frozen (as described above)
1 tablespoon pale tahini
200 ml (7 fl oz) spring or filtered water

Liquidize the ingredients until thick and smooth.

111

Sunflower Milk *Makes 750 ml (1¼ pints)*

This makes a very pleasant white milk which is particularly good over breakfast cererals.

50 g (2 oz) sunflower seeds
600 ml (1 pint) spring or filtered water
a dash of honey, date syrup or maple syrup

Put the sunflower seeds into a food processor or blender with about a third of the water and whizz to a thick purée, then add the rest of the water and whizz again. Sweeten with honey, date syrup or maple syrup if you like, and chill until needed.

Peach-Berry Shake *Makes 1 large or 2 small glasses*

1 ripe peach, stoned, skinned and cut into rough chunks
100 – 225 g (4 – 8 oz) strawberries or raspberries, washed
200 ml (7 fl oz) spring or filtered water, freshly squeezed orange juice or home-made Nut Milk (page 108)

Put the peach and berries into the liquidizer with the water, orange juice or Nut Milk and whizz until thick and smooth. Thin with a little water if necessary.

3

Fruit Salads

Energy Fruit Salad   *Serves 2*

1 Cox or Russet apple, washed, cored and sliced
1 banana, peeled and sliced
1 orange, peeled and chopped
2 tablespoons raisins
freshly squeezed juice of 1 orange

Mix together and serve at once

Pear and Grape Salad   *Serves 1*

1 large, ripe pear, peeled, cored and sliced
100 g (4 oz) black grapes, washed, halved and seeded
freshly squeezed juice of 1 orange

Mix together and serve at once.

Apple, Strawberry and Kiwi Salad   *Serves 2*

1 apple, peeled and cored
225 g (8 oz) strawberries, hulled, washed and sliced
2 kiwi fruits, peeled and sliced
freshly squeezed juice of 1 orange

Mix together and serve at once.

Fruit Platter with Mango Sauce   *Serves 2 – 4*

This makes an attractive dish for a special breakfast or dessert.

3 or 4 types of fresh fruit selected from: 1 banana, a bunch of
black or green grapes, a punnet of strawberries, 1 – 2 sweet
apples, 2 kiwi fruit, 1 – 2 peaches or nectarines, or other fruits
in season
juice of 1 lemon
For the sauce
1 quantity Mango Whizz (page 110)

Prepare the sauce as described. This can be made in advance
and refrigerated until needed.

   Just before serving, prepare the fruit, washing it and cutting
it into medium-sized slices. Dip the slices in lemon juice to stop
them turning brown.

   To serve, pour some of the mango sauce on to a shallow
platter or individual plates. Arrange the pieces of fruit on top
and serve any remaining sauce in a jug.

4

Salad Dressings and Dips

Avocado Dressing · *Serves 4–6*

1 large ripe avocado, halved, stoned and skinned
juice of ½ lemon
1 tablespoon rice vinegar or cider vinegar
1 tablespoon cold-pressed olive oil
sea salt and freshly ground black pepper

Put the avocado into the blender or food processor with the rest of the ingredients. Whizz until thick and creamy.

Vinaigrette · *Serves 4*

3 tablespoons olive oil
1–2 tablespoons red wine vinegar, lemon juice or rice vinegar
a pinch of dried mustard (optional)
sea salt and freshly ground black pepper

Mix all the ingredients together. An easy way to do this is to put them all into a small screw-top jar and shake.

Thick Mustard Vinaigrette   *Serves 4 – 6*

1 tablespoon Dijon mustard (preferably Grey Poupon)
2 tablespoons red wine vinegar
6 tablespoons olive oil (not best quality)
sea salt and freshly ground black pepper

Put the mustard into a bowl and add the vinegar. Then gradually mix in the oil until thick and creamy. Season with salt and pepper.

Japanese Dressing   *Makes 150 ml (5 fl oz)*

1 garlic clove, peeled
a piece of fresh ginger the size of a hazel nut, peeled
1 tablespoon tamari
¼ red pepper
150 ml (5 fl oz) rice vinegar

Put all the ingredients into a food processor or liquidizer and whizz until blended. This dressing keeps well in a screw-top jar in the fridge.

VARIATION

Mustard Dressing

Omit the red pepper and ginger, and instead add 1 – 2 tablespoons Dijon mustard (Grey Poupon, if you can get it) and 1 – 2 teaspoons whole mustard seeds, if available.

Honey Dressing   *Serves 2 – 4*

1 tablespoon raw organic honey
1 – 2 tablespoons freshly squeezed lemon juice, cider vinegar or rice vinegar

Mix the ingredients together until blended, either in a small bowl, or by shaking them in a screw-top jar.

Guacamole   *Serves 3 – 4*

This is delicious as a dip, served with tortilla chips or fresh vegetables, such as small radishes with leaves still attached, florets of cauliflower or mangetout peas. It can also be used as a dressing over salad.

1 large ripe avocado, halved, stoned and skinned
1 tomato, skinned (as described on page 131)
1 garlic clove, peeled
½ – 1 green chilli, washed, halved and de-seeded
2 – 3 tablespoons lemon juice
sea salt and freshly ground black pepper
chopped fresh coriander to garnish

If you are using a food processor, cut the avocado and tomato into chunks, combine with the garlic, chilli and lemon juice and whizz until smooth. Alternatively, mash the avocado and tomato with a fork, then add the crushed garlic, finely chopped chilli and lemon juice. Season with salt and pepper, spoon into a small serving dish and sprinkle with chopped fresh coriander.

Note: The juice of the chilli can irritate your eyes so take care not to touch, and wash your hands after preparing it.

Hummus   *Serves 4–6*

Serve this creamy textured dip with strips of warm pitta bread
or some vegetable crudités, such as carrot sticks, spring onions
and cauliflower florets. Alternatively, try it as a topping for
baked potatoes, or as one of several dishes to make up a
complete meal.

1 × 425 g (15 oz) can chick peas, or 100 g (4 oz) dried chick
peas (prepared and cooked as described on pages 166–7)
1–2 garlic cloves, peeled
2 tablespoons pale tahini
juice of 1–2 lemons
sea salt and freshly ground black pepper
olive oil and paprika pepper to garnish

Drain the chick peas, keeping the liquid. Put the chick peas,
garlic, tahini and lemon juice into a food processor and blend
until creamy. Add some of the reserved liquid if necessary, to
get a light consistency, like softly whipped cream. Season with
salt and pepper. Spoon into a shallow serving dish and top
with a little olive oil and a sprinkling of paprika pepper if liked.

Note: Cypressa tahini is rather milder than the darker types
and can be used in fairly generous quantities. If you can only
get one of the darker tahinis, add cautiously to taste, beginning
with as little as 1 teaspoonful.

Tofu and Cucumber Dip

Serves 2 as a light main course, 4 – 6 as a first course

A deliciously light and creamy pale green dip which can also be used as a salad dressing.

1 packet silken tofu
1 – 2 garlic cloves, peeled
½ cucumber, washed and cut into chunks
1 tablespoon fresh dill or mint, or 1 teaspoon dried dill weed
sea salt and freshly ground black pepper
To serve
½ cucumber, washed and cut into sticks
2 beefsteak tomatoes, sliced

Put the tofu into a food processor with the garlic, cucumber and herbs and whizz until thick and smooth. Season with salt and pepper.

To serve, pour on to individual plates and surround with the cucumber and tomato. Alternatively, the dip can be served in a bowl, with a selection of crudités.

5

Salads

Mixed Salad   *Serves 1*

¼ hearty lettuce, washed and torn or shredded
¼ onion, purple if possible, peeled and sliced thinly
½ firm beefsteak tomato, washed and sliced
any chopped herbs available, especially fresh basil
sea salt and freshly ground black pepper
olive oil
lemon juice

Arrange the lettuce, onion and tomato on a plate. Sprinkle the herbs, if available, on top, and season lightly with salt and pepper. A little olive oil and a squeeze of lemon juice can be added at the table.

Tomato Salad   *Serves 1*

1 firm beefsteak tomato or 2 ordinary tomatoes, washed and sliced
chopped fresh basil, if available
sea salt and freshly ground black pepper
olive oil
lemon juice

Mix the tomato with the basil, if available. Season lightly with salt and pepper. A little olive oil and a squeeze of lemon juice can be added at the table.

Tomato and Coconut Salad   *Serves 1*

1 firm beefsteak tomato or 2 ordinary tomatoes, washed and sliced
a squeeze of lemon juice
sea salt and freshly ground black pepper
1 – 2 teaspoons desiccated coconut

Arrange the slices of tomato on a plate and squeeze over a little lemon juice. Season with salt and pepper and sprinkle with coconut.

Tomato and Onion Salad   *Serves 1*

1 firm beefsteak tomato or 2 ordinary tomatoes, washed and sliced
¼ onion, peeled and sliced thinly
chopped fresh basil, if available
sea salt and freshly ground black pepper
olive oil
lemon juice

Arrange the tomato and onion on a plate. Sprinkle the fresh basil, if you have it, on top, and season lightly with salt and pepper. A little olive oil and a squeeze of lemon juice can be added at the table.

Green Salad   *Serves 1*

¼ hearty lettuce, washed and torn or shredded
any other leafy green vegetables available: a little watercress,
tender spinach, nasturtium, sorrel or dandelion leaves
a little chopped onion or spring onion (optional)
chopped fresh herbs, if available
olive oil
lemon juice or rice vinegar
sea salt and freshly ground black pepper

Put the lettuce and other leaves in a bowl with the onion, if
using, and the chopped fresh herbs if available. Dress with a
few drops of olive oil, a squeeze of lemon juice or a little rice
vinegar and some salt and pepper.

VARIATIONS

With the addition of avocado, seeds or nuts, or a few sprouted
beans or seeds, a green salad becomes a substantial, health-
giving main course. Serve it alone, or with another salad, such
as Carrot (opposite), or with a little plain Steamed Brown Rice
(page 180) or millet, or crusty bread, Garlic Bread (page 137)
or a baked potato (page 161).

Green Salad with Avocado

Add ½ – 1 ripe avocado (halved, stoned, skinned and sliced)
to the salad.

Green Salad with Alfalfa Sprouts

This is a particularly pleasant combination. Just add a handful
of alfalfa sprouts to the basic green salad.

Green Salad with Nuts and Seeds

Add 25 – 50 g (1 – 2 oz) nuts and/or seeds to the salad. Choose one type, or a mixture, such as pine nuts, sunflower seeds and pumpkin seeds; chopped pecan nuts and sesame seeds; walnuts, almonds and pumpkin seeds; chopped pistachio nuts and pine nuts; or whatever you fancy.

Alfalfa and Carrot Salad   *Serves 1*

2 – 3 carrots, scraped and coarsely grated
a good handful of alfalfa sprouts
olive oil
lemon juice or rice vinegar
sea salt and freshly ground black pepper

Put the grated carrot and alfalfa into a bowl and mix together. Dress with a few drops of olive oil, a squeeze of lemon juice or a little rice vinegar and some salt and pepper.

Carrot Salad   *Serves 1*

2 – 3 large carrots, scraped and coarsely grated
¼ red pepper, washed and chopped, or 1 – 2 sticks celery, washed and sliced (optional)
lemon juice
olive oil
sea salt and freshly ground black pepper

Mix the carrots with the pepper or celery if using. Sprinkle with a little lemon juice, olive oil and some salt and pepper.

Carrot and Mustard Seed Salad   *Serves 2*

6 large carrots, scraped and coarsely grated
1 tablespoon olive oil
4 teaspoons whole mustard seeds, white or black
sea salt and freshly ground black pepper

Put the carrot in a bowl. Heat the olive oil, then put in the mustard seeds. Stir for a moment or two until the seeds start to pop, then pour them, and the oil, over the carrots. Season lightly with salt and pepper and stir well.

Multicoloured Salad   *Serves 1*

This can be made from any fresh, raw vegetables. Choose 4 or 5 types, with as much contrast in colour and texture as possible

1 carrot, scraped and finely diced or coarsely grated
3 – 4 baby sweetcorn, washed and sliced
2 – 3 lettuce leaves, washed and shredded
a few cauliflower or broccoli florets, washed and chopped
a few radishes, washed and cut into circles
a little cucumber, washed and cubed
a few sprouted beans or seeds if available
chopped fresh herbs, if available
sea salt and freshly ground black pepper

Mix all the ingredients together. You can add a squeeze of lemon juice or a dash of olive oil if you like, but this salad is also nice without a dressing.

Spinach Salad   *Serves 2*

½ bunch (100 – 175 g or 4 – 6 oz) tender spinach, washed and shredded
1 large tomato, washed and chopped
½ onion, peeled and chopped
1 small raw beetroot, skinned and coarsely grated (optional)
2 – 3 tablespoons rice vinegar
1 tablespoon olive oil
sea salt and freshly ground black pepper

Mix all the ingredients together in a bowl.

Vitamin Salad   *Serves 1*

2 large carrots, scraped and grated
1 raw beetroot, skinned and grated
a handful of sprouted beans or seeds
any other raw vegetables available: lettuce leaves, sliced tomato, cauliflower, celery, onion, fennel
1 tablespoon olive oil
1 tablespoon lemon juice
1 sheet nori, if available

Mix all the vegetables together, or place in separate piles on a plate. Mix together the oil and vinegar and pour over the salad. If you are using nori, hold it over a gas flame or electric hotplate for a few seconds until it becomes crisp and crunchy, then crumble it over the salad. Serve at once.

Cabbage Salad   *Serves 4*

350 g (12 oz) white cabbage, washed and finely shredded
100 g (4 oz) carrots, scraped and coarsely grated
4 tablespoons Vinaigrette (page 115), Thick Mustard Vinaigrette (page 116), Honey Dressing (page 117), or Japanese Dressing (page 116)
sea salt and freshly ground black pepper

Just put all the ingredients in a bowl and mix together.

Radish, Cucumber and Hiziki Salad   *Serves 4*

Don't be put off by the seaweed – hiziki – in this recipe. With a sweet and sour dressing, it makes a very good salad, full of nutrients, and looks pretty with the cucumber and radishes. Excellent for serving with oriental-style rice dishes, hiziki is available in Japanese shops – it looks like a packet of little dried black twigs – or you can send for it by post from Clearspring (page 229).

15 g (½ oz) hiziki
½ cucumber, peeled and diced
1 bunch radishes, washed, trimmed and sliced
1 teaspoon sea salt
1 teaspoon sugar
2 tablespoons rice vinegar

Rinse the hiziki under the cold tap, then soak in cold water for 5 minutes. Drain, place in a saucepan, cover with water, bring to the boil, and simmer gently for 10 minutes. Drain and cool. Add the cucumber, radishes, salt, sugar and vinegar to the hiziki, mix well, and serve.

Avocado Vinaigrette Salad   *Serves 1*

This makes a filling and delicious main-course meal.

A whole small avocado, halved and stoned, or half a large one, stoned
A few lettuce leaves, washed
1 – 2 carrots, scraped and coarsely grated
1 – 2 tomatoes, washed and sliced
lemon juice
olive oil
sea salt and freshly ground black pepper

Place the avocado on a base of lettuce and surround with the grated carrot and sliced tomato. Dress with a little lemon juice and olive oil and season with salt and pepper. Serve at once.

Tomato-Cucumber-Avocado Salad   *Serves 2*

This is filling and makes a good main course on its own, or with some plain wholewheat bread or brown rice if you want to make it more substantial.

1 – 2 large beefsteak tomatoes, washed and sliced
1 large ripe avocado, halved, stoned, skinned and sliced
½ – 1 large cucumber, washed and cut into thin diagonal slices
lemon juice
olive oil
sea salt and freshly ground black pepper

Arrange the slices of tomato, avocado and cucumber on a plate. Sprinkle with lemon juice, a little olive oil, and some salt and pepper. Serve at once.

Greek Salad with Tofu   *Serves 1*

1 garlic clove, peeled and crushed
1 tablespoon olive oil
1 tablespoon wine vinegar or lemon juice
½ packet, about 75 g (3 oz), firm tofu, drained and cut into cubes
freshly ground black pepper
6 black olives
½ beefsteak tomato, washed and diced
⅓ large cucumber, peeled and diced
½ purple onion, peeled and sliced
sea salt

Put the garlic, oil and vinegar or lemon juice in a bowl. Add the tofu and a good grinding of black pepper, and mix gently. Then add the remaining ingredients and season with a little salt if necessary.

VARIATIONS

Greek Salad with Butterbeans

Instead of the tofu, use ½ × 425 g (15 oz) can or 175 – 225 g (6 – 8 oz) drained cooked butterbeans.

Greek Salad with Avocado

Instead of the tofu, use ½ – 1 ripe avocado, stoned, skinned and chopped.

Big, Beautiful Biogenic Salad   *Serves 1*

This is very filling and makes a quick, healthy main course.
Serve it with a baked potato or some good wholewheat bread,
or add a few sunflower seeds or chopped nuts to the mixture.

a good handful of sprouted beans or seeds
2 – 3 large carrots, scraped and coarsely grated
any other raw vegetable available: lettuce, tender spinach,
watercress, celery, spring onion, cauliflower, broccoli, tomato,
fennel, pepper, cucumber, chicory, chopped or shredded
chopped fresh herbs, if available
1 garlic clove, peeled and crushed (optional)
1 tablespoon olive oil
1 – 2 tablespoons lemon juice
sea salt and freshly ground black pepper
a dash of tamari (optional)

Put all the ingredients in a bowl and mix together. This recipe
can be varied in many ways, using whatever fresh ingredients
you have.

Brown Rice, Carrot and Raisin Salad   *Serves 1*

100 g (4 oz) cooked brown rice
2 – 3 large carrots, scraped and coarsely grated
2 sticks celery, washed and sliced
2 – 3 tablespoons raisins
sea salt and freshly ground black pepper
lemon juice

Mix the rice and vegetables together, add the raisins, season
with salt and pepper, and sprinkle with lemon juice to taste.

Bean Salad with Onions and Herbs   *Serves 4*

Serve this nice and cold with some crusty bread on a hot day. Some green salad and a sliced tomato and black olive salad go well with it, to make a complete meal.

2 tablespoons lemon juice
3 tablespoons olive oil
sea salt and freshly ground black pepper
2 × 425 g (15 oz) cans cannellini beans, drained, or 200 g (7 oz) dried cannellini beans, soaked and cooked (see pages 166–7)
1 purple onion, peeled and thinly sliced
1 garlic clove, peeled and crushed
2 heaped tablespoons fresh chopped parsley

Put the lemon juice and oil into a large bowl with some salt and pepper and mix together. Then add all the other ingredients and stir gently.

Bulgur Wheat Salad (Tabbouleh)   *Serves 8*

225 g (8 oz) bulgur wheat
1 teaspoon sea salt
350 ml (12 fl oz) boiling water
450 g (1 lb) tomatoes, washed
½ cucumber, washed
50 ml (2 fl oz) olive oil
50 ml (2 fl oz) lemon juice
2 garlic cloves, peeled and crushed
3 tablespoons finely chopped fresh mint
3 tablespoons finely chopped fresh parsley
1 cos lettuce, washed, to serve

Put the bulgur wheat into a bowl with the salt and add the boiling water. Leave for 15 minutes, to allow the wheat to absorb the water.

Meanwhile, skin the tomatoes by covering them with boiling water, leaving for 1–2 minutes, then slipping off the skins with the aid of a pointed knife. Chop the tomatoes and cut the cucumber into 5 mm (¼ inch) dice. Add the oil, lemon juice, garlic, mint and parsley to the wheat and stir well, then add the tomatoes and cucumber.

To serve, line a dish with cos lettuce leaves and pile the salad on top.

Millet, Carrot and Leek Salad   *Serves 2*

100 g (4 oz) millet (cooked as described on pages 178–9)
350 ml (12 fl oz) boiling water
2 tender leeks, washed
4–6 carrots, scraped
½–1 lettuce, or a handful of green leaves such as tender spinach, washed and chopped
For the dressing
1 garlic clove, peeled and crushed
a small piece of fresh ginger, peeled and grated (optional)
2 tablespoons olive oil
2 tablespoons freshly squeezed lemon juice
1 tablespoon tamari

While the millet is cooking, make the dressing by combining all the ingredients in a bowl. Then slice the leeks finely, including some of the green part, and coarsely grate the carrots. Add the leeks and carrots to the millet (which can still be hot), together with the dressing. Mix well and serve on a base of shredded green leaves – lettuce, spinach or whatever is available.

Mediterranean Rice Salad

Serves 4

Serve this delicious salad as it is, or with some shredded lettuce and warm crusty bread.

1 quantity Steamed Brown Rice (page 180)
2 garlic cloves, peeled and crushed
3 tablespoons olive oil
1 – 2 tablespoons lemon juice
2 beefsteak tomatoes, washed and chopped
1 large purple onion, peeled and sliced
1 red or green pepper, washed and chopped
12 – 16 black olives
sea salt and freshly ground black pepper
chopped fresh parsley or basil

Put the rice in a bowl, add all the other ingredients and mix gently. It doesn't matter if the rice is still hot when you make this salad. Leave it on one side to cool and let the flavours blend.

Spiced Rice Salad

Serves 1

100 g (4 oz) cooked brown rice
½ teaspoon curry powder
¼ onion, peeled and chopped
½ apple, peeled and chopped
½ banana, peeled and chopped
2 – 3 tablespoons raisins
lemon juice
sea salt and freshly ground black pepper
1 – 2 teaspoons desiccated coconut

Mix the rice with the curry powder, onion, apple and banana. Add the raisins and some lemon juice to taste. Season with salt and pepper, and sprinkle with the coconut before serving.

Potato Salad   *Serves 3–4*

Although it's usually served as a side dish, this makes an excellent main course when combined with one or two other salads to set it off: a green salad and either a tomato salad, grated carrot or beetroot salad.

750 g (1½ lb) potatoes, scrubbed or peeled and cut into even-sized pieces
1 quantity Vinaigrette (page 115), or Thick Mustard Vinaigrette (page 116)
sea salt and freshly ground black pepper
chopped fresh parsley or chives (optional)

Put the potatoes in a large pan. Cover with water and cook until they are only just tender, then drain immediately. Let the potatoes cool slightly, cut them into smaller pieces if you wish, and put them in a bowl. Add the vinaigrette, salt and pepper to taste and stir gently until the potato is coated with the dressing. Put all the ingredients in a bowl and mix together. Snip a little parsley or chives over the top, if you like. Cool completely before serving.

6

Bread and Sandwich Snacks

Salad Sandwiches   *Serves 1*

2 lettuce leaves
2 large slices wholewheat bread
1 large tomato, washed and sliced
a few slices raw onion
2 – 3 slices avocado (optional)
sea salt and freshly ground black pepper

Put a lettuce leaf on top of each slice of bread, then heap the
rest of the filling ingredients on one of the slices of bread. Top
with the other and press down well. Cut in half and serve.
Some grated carrot, beansprouts, cucumber or any other fresh
vegetable ingredients can be added to the sandwich if you wish.

OTHER SANDWICH FILLINGS

–Tahini and sprouted mung beans or alfalfa
–A thin layer of miso or yeast extract with sliced cucumber or
cress
–Peanut butter and sliced cucumber, grated carrot or chopped
celery

—Thin slices of cold Lentil Loaf (page 171) or Nut Roast (page 191) and pickle, chutney and sliced tomato and/or onion
—Hummus (page 118)
—Finely sliced mushrooms fried in olive oil, with or without garlic, and cooled
—Cold cooked asparagus spears tossed in Vinaigrette (page 115)
—Tahini and chopped dates
—Sliced banana and finely grated hazel nuts
—Sliced banana and tahini or peanut butter
—Raw organic honey and grated nuts

Pitta Pocket Filled with Sprouted Chick Peas   *Serves 1*

1 wholemeal pitta bread
2 – 3 lettuce leaves, washed and shredded
1 large tomato, washed and sliced
¼ onion, washed and sliced
a handful of sprouted chick peas
1 garlic clove, peeled and crushed
a squeeze of lemon juice
a few slices avocado (optional)
sea salt and freshly ground black pepper

Slit the pitta bread at the top and ease it open, to make a pocket for the filling. In a bowl mix together the lettuce, tomato, onion, sprouted chick peas, garlic, lemon juice and avocado, if using, season with salt and pepper, and pack the mixture into the pitta bread.

If you plan to eat the pitta pocket straight away, you may like to make the filling, then briefly warm the pitta in the oven, under the grill or in a toaster. When warm, slit open the pocket and fill.

Toasted Avocado Sandwich

Serves 1

½ ripe avocado, stoned, skinned and mashed
1 – 2 teaspoons lemon juice
sea salt and freshly ground black pepper
1 spring onion, finely chopped
2 slices wholewheat bread
olive oil

Heat a toasted-sandwich-maker. Mix the avocado with the lemon juice, salt and pepper, and spring onion. Spread the avocado mixture on the slices of bread and sandwich together. Brush the sandwich-maker with olive oil. Put the sandwich in the sandwich-maker for 4 – 5 minutes, until crisp and golden brown. Serve at once.

FILLINGS FOR TOASTED SANDWICHES

–Chopped fried mushrooms
–Mashed cooked asparagus
–Hummus (page 118)
–Guacamole (page 117)
–Beans mashed with garlic or pickle
–Sliced tomato

Garlic Bread   *Serves 6*

1 wholewheat French stick
3 – 4 garlic cloves, peeled
100 ml (3½ fl oz) olive oil

Set the oven to 200°C/400°F/Gas Mark 6.
   Make slices in the French stick 2.5 cm (1 inch) apart, almost cutting through but making sure that the slices are still joined at the base. Crush the garlic and mix with the oil, or whizz the whole garlic cloves and olive oil in a blender until the garlic is puréed. Brush the garlic oil over each cut surface of bread.
   Then push the slices together to reform the loaf, wrap it in greaseproof paper, place on a baking tray and bake for about 20 minutes, or until the bread has heated through and is crisp. Serve at once.

Individual Garlic Bread   *Serves 1*

½ – 1 garlic clove, peeled and crushed
1 tablespoon olive oil
1 slice wholewheat bread

Mix together the garlic and oil and brush over the bread. Put the bread under a hot grill for 2 – 3 minutes until crisp on top and heated through.

Filled Wholewheat French Stick

Serves 1

10 – 15 cm (4 – 6 inch) wholewheat stick
a little Dijon mustard
2 – 3 lettuce leaves, washed and shredded
1 large tomato, washed and sliced
¼ onion, peeled and sliced
5 cm (2 inch) piece of cucumber, washed and chopped
a handful of sprouted beans (optional)
a few slices avocado, chopped (optional)
sea salt and freshly ground black pepper

Make a slit down the side of the French stick and scoop out a little of the crumb. Spread the inside of the bread with a very thin layer of mustard. Fill with the salad ingredients, seasoning lightly with salt and pepper. Press the two pieces together and serve.

7

Soups

Quick Lentil Soup   *Serves 4*

This can be made in 10 minutes with a pressure cooker, or half an hour in a saucepan. It makes a lovely warming lunch or a quick supper on a cold day. It's good with wholewheat Garlic Bread (page 137) and some crunchy crudités: sticks of carrot, celery and some spring onions.

2 onions, peeled and chopped
1 tablespoon olive oil
2 carrots, scraped and sliced
225 g (8 oz) red lentils
1 litre (1¾ pints) spring or filtered water
2 garlic cloves, peeled
sea salt and freshly ground black pepper

Fry the onions in the oil for 5 minutes, then add the carrots. Cook for a moment or two, and add the lentils and water. Then bring to the boil and simmer for about 20 minutes, or cook in a pressure cooker for 5 minutes.

Liquidize the soup with the garlic. Return to the pan, reheat, and season with salt and pepper.

VARIATION

Spicy Lentil Soup

For a delicious spicy version, make the soup as described. Then, just before serving, fry a small chopped onion and 2−3 crushed garlic cloves in 1 tablespoon olive oil. Add 1−2 teaspoons ground cumin and the seeds from 1−2 coriander pods, if you have them. Stir over the heat for 1−2 minutes, then stir into the soup.

Green Pea Soup with Mint   *Serves 4*

1 onion, peeled and chopped
1 tablespoon olive oil
1 large potato, peeled and diced
450 g (1 lb) frozen peas
600 ml (1 pint) spring or filtered water
a small bunch of fresh mint
sea salt and freshly ground black pepper
a pinch of sugar

Fry the onion gently in the oil for 5 minutes, then add the potato. Cover and cook for a further 5−10 minutes without browning. Add the peas, water and half the mint, and bring to the boil. Then cover and cook gently for about 15 minutes, until the potato is tender.

Liquidize the soup (including the mint sprigs), and, for a smooth, velvety texture, pass through a sieve. Season with salt, pepper and a pinch of sugar, and snip the rest of the mint over the top before serving.

Tomato Soup   *Serves 4*

1 onion, peeled and chopped
1 tablespoon olive oil
350 g (12 oz) potatoes, peeled and diced
450 g (1 lb) tomatoes, skinned (as described on page 131) and sliced, or 1 × 400 g (14 oz) can tomatoes
900 ml (1½ pints) vegetable stock or filtered/spring water
sea salt and freshly ground black pepper

Fry the onion in the oil in a large saucepan, covered, for 5 minutes, without browning. Add the potatoes, cover again and cook gently for a further 5 – 10 minutes, then add the tomatoes and cook for a further 4 – 5 minutes. Stir from time to time and do not allow the vegetables to brown. Add the stock or water, cover the pan and leave the soup to simmer for 15 – 20 minutes, or until the potatoes are tender.

Liquidize the soup, and if you want it really smoth, sieve it to remove the tomato seeds (this isn't essential). Reheat the soup gently without boiling, season with salt and pepper, and serve.

Watercress Soup   *Serves 4*

1 onion, peeled and chopped
1 tablespoon olive oil
750 g (1½ lb) potatoes, peeled and diced
900 ml (1½ pints) stock or filtered/spring water
a bunch of watercress
sea salt and freshly ground black pepper

Fry the onion in the oil in a large saucepan, covered, for 5 minutes, without browning. Add the potatoes, cover again and cook gently for a further 5 – 10 minutes. Stir from time to time and do not allow the vegetables to brown. Stir in the stock or water and leave the soup to simmer for about 20 minutes, or until the potatoes are tender. Liquidize the soup with the watercress. Season with salt and pepper to taste.

Green Soup   *Serves 4*

1 onion, peeled and chopped
1 tablespoon olive oil
225 g (8 oz) potatoes, peeled and diced
a handful of spinach leaves, or outer leaves of 1 large lettuce, roughly chopped
900 ml (1½ pints) filtered or spring water
sea salt and freshly ground black pepper
freshly grated nutmeg, if available

Fry the onion in the oil in a large saucepan, covered, for 5 minutes, without browning. Then add the potato and spinach or lettuce and fry for a further 5 minutes. Bring to the boil and simmer gently, covered, for about 15 minutes, or until the potatoes are tender. Liquidize and season with salt, pepper and nutmeg if available.

Carrot Soup   *Serves 4 – 6*

1 onion, peeled and chopped
1 tablespoon olive oil
225 g (8 oz) potatoes, peeled and diced
450 g (1 lb) carrots, scraped and chopped
1.2 litres (2 pints) filtered or spring water
1 tablespoon lemon juice
sea salt and freshly ground black pepper

Fry the onion in the oil, in a large saucepan, covered, for 5 minutes, without browning. Then add the potatoes and carrots, cover, and cook gently for a further 5 – 10 minutes. Add the water, bring to the boil, then cover the pan and leave the soup to simmer for about 15 minutes, or until the potatoes are tender. Liquidize the soup, add the lemon juice, and season to taste with salt and pepper.

Beetroot Soup   *Serves 4 – 6*

1 onion, peeled and chopped
1 tablespoon olive oil
225 g (8 oz) potatoes, peeled and diced
450 g (1 lb) cooked beetroot, skinned and diced
1.2 litres (2 pints) filtered or spring water
1 tablespoon lemon juice
sea salt and freshly ground black pepper

Fry the onion in the oil, in a large saucepan, covered, for 5 minutes, without browning. Then add the potatoes, cover, and cook gently for a further 5 – 10 minutes. Add the beetroot and water, bring to the boil, then cover the pan and leave the soup to simmer for about 15 minutes, or until the potatoes are tender. Liquidize the soup, add the lemon juice, and season to taste with salt and pepper.

Vegetable Soup   *Serves 4*

1 onion, peeled and chopped
1 tablespoon olive oil
1 carrot, scraped and diced
1 small turnip, peeled and diced
1 small potato, peeled and diced
a small piece of celery, washed and diced
1 small leek, washed and sliced
1 small courgette, washed and diced
1 litre (1¾ pints) filtered or spring water
1 large tomato, skinned (as described on page 131) and chopped
a little lemon juice
sea salt and freshly ground black pepper

Fry the onion in the oil in a large saucepan, covered, for 5 minutes, without browning. Then add the rest of the vegetables except for the tomato, cover and cook for a further 5 minutes. Add the water and simmer for 5 – 10 minutes, or until the vegetables are tender. Add the tomato, a squeeze of lemon juice, and season to taste with salt and pepper.

Soupe au Pistou   *Serves 4*

This wonderful, easy-to-make and very filling vegetable soup from the South of France reheats well and tastes even better the next day. Serve it with crusty bread for a complete main course.

1 onion, peeled and chopped
2 tablespoons olive oil
125 g (4 oz) dried haricot beans, soaked and cooked (as described on pages 166–7), or 1 × 425 g (15 oz) can cannellini beans
2 carrots, scraped and diced
2 potatoes, peeled and diced
3 leeks or courgettes, washed and sliced
450 g (1 lb) tomatoes, skinned (as described on page 131) and chopped, or 1 × 425 g (15 oz) can tomatoes
2 garlic cloves, peeled and crushed
sea salt and freshly ground black pepper
1 teaspoon dried basil or 1–2 tablespoons chopped fresh basil
1 litre (1¾ pints) filtered or spring water
50 g (2 oz) thin pasta or pasta shapes

Fry the onions in the oil in a large saucepan, covered, for 5 minutes, without browning. Then add the drained beans, all the vegetables, the garlic, some salt and pepper, and the basil if you're using dried, cover, and cook for a further 5 minutes. Add the water (you can use the water drained from the beans as part of this) and simmer for 20–30 minutes. Then add the pasta and cook for a further 10 minutes. If you're using fresh basil, add this now; season to taste with salt and pepper.

Oriental Broth   *Serves 4*

This savoury soup is light but sustaining. It is also extremely easy to make.

4 pieces wakame seaweed, if available
275 g (10 oz) firm tofu
2 spring onions
900 ml (1½ pints) filtered or spring water
4 tablespoons miso
1 teaspoon tamari

Soak the wakame in a little cold water for 10 minutes, drain, then cut out and discard the spine and any hard pieces. Snip roughly with kitchen scissors and divide the pieces of wakame between 4 soup bowls. Cut the tofu into 16 cubes and put 4 in each bowl, then chop the spring onions and add these to the bowls, too.

Heat the water in a saucepan, then take out a little and blend with the miso, to soften and make a creamy consistency. Tip this back into the saucepan with the rest of the water. Bring the soup almost to the boil, but do not let it boil, or valuable enzymes in the miso will be destroyed. Add the tamari, then pour the soup into the bowls over the tofu and chopped spring onions. Serve immediately.

8

Light Vegetable Dishes

Garlic Mushrooms

Serves 1–2 as a main course

Garlic mushrooms are filling and make a delicious main course if you serve them with warm crusty bread and a good green salad.

2 tablespoons olive oil
450 g (1 lb) button mushrooms, washed, dried and any larger ones halved or quartered
1–2 large garlic cloves, peeled and crushed
sea salt and freshly ground black pepper

Heat the oil in a large saucepan or frying pan, and put in the mushrooms and garlic. Stir all the time, for about 3–4 minutes, until the mushrooms are hot and beginning to get tender. Season with salt and pepper, and serve immediately.

VARIATION

Mushrooms à la Grecque

Crush 1 tablespoon coriander seeds in a pestle and mortar, or on a board with a wooden spoon. Then make as described, but fry the crushed coriander seeds in the oil for 1 – 2 minutes before adding the mushrooms, and sprinkle the mushrooms with the juice of ½ a lemon. Serve hot or cold.

Ragout of Mushrooms   *Serves 2*

1 tablespoon olive oil
1 onion, peeled and chopped
1 garlic clove, peeled and crushed
450 g (1 lb) button mushrooms, washed and any larger ones halved or quartered
2 tomatoes, skinned (as described on page 131) and chopped
1 teaspoon cornflour
sea salt and freshly ground black pepper
chopped fresh parsley to garnish (optional)

Heat the oil in a large saucepan or frying pan and fry the onion for 5 minutes. Add the garlic and mushrooms, and fry for a further 5 minutes. Mix together the tomatoes and cornflour and add to the saucepan, stirring well. Then stir over the heat for 1 – 2 minutes, or until the mixture has thickened slightly. Season with salt and pepper, sprinkle with chopped parsley, if using, and serve.

Beansprout Stir-Fry   *Serves 1*

1 tablespoon olive oil
1 garlic clove, peeled and crushed
175 g (6 oz) beansprouts or any type of sprouted beans and/or seeds
2 spring onions, washed and sliced
1 carrot, scraped and coarsely grated or cut into thin matchsticks
1 medium courgette, washed and coarsely grated or cut into thin matchsticks
1 tablespoon tamari
sea salt and freshly ground black pepper

Heat the oil in a large saucepan or frying pan, add the garlic and fry for a few seconds. Add the beansprouts (or other type of sprouts) and fry for 1 minute. Then add the carrot and courgettes and stir-fry for about 2 minutes, or until the vegetables are all heated through and slightly tender. Sprinkle with the tamari. Season with salt and pepper and serve.

Red Cabbage Stir-Fry   *Serves 2*

450 g (1 lb) red cabbage
heart of 1 celery
1 small sweet apple
2 tablespoons olive oil
2 tablespoons wine vinegar
salt and freshly ground black pepper

Shred the cabbage fairly finely; chop the celery. Keep on one side until just before you are ready to serve the meal, then dice the apple. Heat the oil in a saucepan, then add the cabbage, celery and apple and stir-fry for 2–4 minutes. Add the vinegar and season to taste.

Special Vegetable Stir-Fry   *Serves 2*

This is delicious on its own, or, for a more filling meal, with brown rice.

100 g (4 oz) broccoli, washed
1 tablespoon olive oil
1 garlic clove, peeled and crushed
100 g (4 oz) small thin French beans, washed, topped and tailed
100 g (4 oz) carrots, scraped and sliced diagonally
1 red pepper, washed, cored, seeded and cut into strips
100 g (4 oz) mangetout peas, washed, topped and tailed
100 g (4 oz) asparagus, washed, trimmed and the stems sliced diagonally
4 spring onions, sliced diagonally
grated rind of ½ lemon
sea salt and freshly ground black pepper

Take the florets off the broccoli and leave on one side. Cut the stems into thin matchsticks. Heat the oil, fry the garlic and stir for a second or two. Then add the broccoli matchsticks, French beans, carrots and pepper and stir-fry for 2 minutes. Next, add the mangetout peas, asparagus, broccoli florets and spring onions, and stir-fry for a further 2 minutes. Sprinkle over the grated lemon rind, season with salt and pepper, and serve at once.

Stir-Fried Chinese Vegetables   *Serves 2*

This is good just as it is, or with some plain boiled rice, for a more filling meal. If you're serving brown rice with it, you'll need to get that started about 40 minutes before you make the stir-fried vegetables, because they cook very quickly.

2 tablespoons olive oil
1 × 200 g (7 oz) packet firm tofu, drained and cubed
1 onion, peeled and sliced
2 carrots, scraped and sliced diagonally
1 garlic clove, peeled and crushed (optional)
½ – 1 teaspoon fresh grated ginger (optional)
100 g (4 oz) baby sweetcorn, washed and halved if large
100 g (4 oz) baby button mushrooms, washed
1 can (227 g) water chestnuts, drained
1 can (227 g) bamboo shoots, drained
1 teaspoon cornflour
2 tablespoons tamari

Heat the oil in a frying pan and fry the tofu until browned all over, turning frequently. Take the tofu out of the pan with a draining spoon and leave on one side. Fry the onion and carrots for 5 – 10 minutes, or until just softening. Then add the garlic and ginger, if using, the sweetcorn, mushrooms, water chestnuts and bamboo shoots and cook for 1 – 2 minutes to heat through. Meanwhile, blend the cornflour with the tamari, and add to the pan, stirring. Add the fried tofu and stir gently until heated through. Serve immediately.

Hot Stuffed Avocado   *Serves 2*

Take care not to overcook the avocado – it should be baked just long enough to heat through. It is good served with some steamed vegetables or on a base of cooked spinach or Swiss chard.

1 spring onion, washed and finely chopped
100 g (4 oz) button mushrooms, washed and sliced
1 tablespoon olive oil
½ teaspoon curry powder
2 tablespoons sultanas (optional)
1 large ripe avocado, halved and stoned
1 tablespoon dry sherry or lemon juice
sea salt and freshly ground black pepper

Set the oven to 200°C/400°F/Gas Mark 6.
   Fry the spring onion and mushrooms in the oil for 3–4 minutes, or until just softening. Then add the curry powder and sultanas, if using, fry for a further 1 minute, and remove from the heat.
   Meanwhile, use a teaspoon to scoop the flesh out of the avocado halves without damaging the skins. Dice the flesh and add to the mushroom mixture, together with the sherry or lemon juice. Season to taste with salt and pepper. Pile the mixture back into the skins, place them in a shallow ovenproof dish and bake for 10–15 minutes. Serve at once.

9

Vegetable Stews and Hotpots

Ratatouille   *Serves 4*

This is quick and easy to make, filling and a very good basis
for variations. Ratatouille is good with warm wholewheat
bread, potatoes boiled or baked in their skins, brown rice,
bulgur wheat or millet. It is equally good the next day, heated
or cold.

2 large onions, peeled and chopped
450 g (1 lb) red peppers, washed, cored, seeded and sliced
3 tablespoons olive oil
3 garlic cloves, peeled and crushed
450 g (1 lb) courgettes or marrow, cut into even-sized pieces
450 g (1 lb) aubergines, diced
750 g (1½ lb) tomatoes, skinned (see page 131) and chopped
sea salt and freshly ground black pepper
chopped fresh parsley to garnish

In a large pan, gently fry the onions and peppers in the oil for
5 minutes. Then add the garlic, courgettes or marrow, and
aubergines. Stir, then cover the saucepan and cook for 20 – 25
minutes, or until all the vegetables are tender. Add the
tomatoes and cook, uncovered, for a further 4 – 5 minutes, to
heat the tomatoes through. Season with salt and pepper,
sprinkle with chopped parsley and serve.

VARIATIONS

Spicy Ratatouille

Add 2 – 3 teaspoons ground coriander with the garlic for a delicious, lightly spiced version.

Ratatouille with Mushrooms

Fry 100 – 225 g (4 – 8 oz) sliced button mushrooms in 1 – 2 tablespoons olive oil and add to the ratatouille just before serving.

Ratatouille with Potatoes

Add 225 – 450 g (8 oz – 1 lb) new potatoes, cut into walnut-sized pieces, with the courgettes or marrow. Make sure they are tender – but not soggy or broken up – before serving.

Red Cabbage Casserole   *Serves 4 – 6*

1 red cabbage, about 1 kg (2 – 2¼ lb), washed, cored and shredded
1 large onion, peeled and chopped
2 tablespoons olive oil
1 eating apple, peeled, cored and chopped (optional)
50 g (2 oz) raisins or sultanas (optional)
2 tablespoons lemon juice, cider vinegar or rice wine vinegar
sea salt, a pinch of brown sugar and freshly ground black pepper

Put the cabbage in a large saucepan, cover with water and bring to the boil, then drain thoroughly. Meanwhile, fry the onion in the oil in a large saucepan for 5 minutes, then add the apple and raisins or sultanas, if using, and the cabbage. Cover and cook very gently for 45 – 60 minutes, or until the cabbage is really tender, stirring occasionally. Add the lemon juice or vinegar, salt, sugar and pepper to taste.

Spinach with Cumin Seeds   *Serves 2 – 4*

This is a pleasantly spiced dish which goes well with Dal (page 169) or with Golden Spiced Potatoes (page 159) or some plain or Spicy Brown Rice (page 180). For a lighter meal, it can be served on its own with a Tomato and Onion Salad (page 121) or Tomato and Coconut Salad (page 121).

1 kg (2 lb) fresh spinach, thoroughly washed
sea salt and freshly ground black pepper
2 onions, peeled and sliced
2 tablespoons olive oil
1 garlic clove, peeled and crushed
2 teaspoons cumin seeds
1 dried red chilli, or a piece of fresh chilli (optional – it's hot!)

Put the spinach, which should still be damp, in a large saucepan without any extra water. Cover and cook for 8 – 10 minutes, or until the spinach is tender. You may need to push it down with the end of a fish slice during the cooking time, so that it all cooks evenly. Drain the spinach thoroughly and season it with salt and pepper.

While the spinach is cooking, fry the onions in the oil for 7 – 8 minutes, or until almost tender. Then add the garlic, cumin and chilli, if using, and cook for a further 2 – 3 minutes.

To serve, put the spinach in a warmed dish and pour the onion and cumin mixture over the top, removing the chilli.

Spiced Vegetables *Serves 4–6*

Don't be put off by the number of ingredients in this recipe. It is very easy to make and one of the most delicious vegetable dishes I know. Serve it on its own or with a Tomato and Onion Salad (page 121), and some brown rice; or as part of a number of spicy dishes, to feed a crowd. This dish tastes even better if made a day in advance and reheated. In fact it can stand several reheatings and tastes better each time!

4 tablespoons olive oil
1 teaspoon white mustard seed
4 teaspoons ground turmeric
2 tablespoons ground coriander
14–16 curry leaves, or ½ teaspoon curry powder
4 garlic cloves, peeled and crushed
4 cm (1½ inch) piece fresh ginger, peeled and grated
1 green chilli, washed, de-seeded and chopped
2 onions, peeled and chopped
750 g (1½ lb) potatoes, scrubbed and cut into even-sized pieces
1 large cauliflower, washed and divided into florets
120 g (4 oz) green beans, washed
2 large carrots, scraped and sliced
8 spinach or cabbage leaves, washed and roughly shredded
200 ml (7 fl oz) filtered or spring water
sea salt and freshly ground black pepper

Heat the oil and fry the spices, garlic, ginger and chilli for 1–2 minutes. Then put in the onions and fry gently for 5 minutes. Add the rest of the ingredients, and turn them so that they all get coated with the spices and oil. Add the water and bring to the boil. Then cover and cook gently for about 15 minutes, or until the vegetables are just tender and most of the liquid has been absorbed. Season with salt and pepper, and serve.

Vegetable Hotpot   *Serves 2*

2 tablespoons olive oil
1 onion, peeled and sliced
1 garlic clove, peeled and crushed
1 large potato, peeled and thinly sliced
2 carrots, scraped and thinly sliced
2 leeks, washed and cut into 1 cm (½ inch) pieces, or 4 – 6
cabbage leaves, washed and shredded
200 ml (7 fl oz) filtered or spring water
sea salt and freshly ground black pepper
chopped fresh parsley to garnish (optional)

Heat the oil in a deep, heavy-based saucepan. Fry the onion
for 5 minutes, then put in the garlic and all the vegetables. Add
the water, season lightly with salt and pepper, and stir. Then
cover and leave to cook gently for 15 – 20 minutes, or until all
the vegetables are tender. Check the seasoning, sprinkle with
parsley and serve.

VARIATIONS

Vegetable Hotpot With Spinach or Swiss Chard

Make as described, using 350 – 450 g (12 oz – 1 lb) spinach or
Swiss chard instead of the leeks or cabbage leaves. Wash
thoroughly; chop both the stalks and the leaves and add with
the potatoes and carrots.

Leek and Potato Hotpot

Make as described, replacing the carrots with an extra potato.

10

Potato Dishes

Potato Bake   *Serves 3*

This makes a healthy and delicious main course when served
with a large green salad or a cooked leafy green vegetable such
as spinach.

3 tablespoons olive oil
1 kg (2 lb) potatoes, peeled and cut into thin slices – no thicker
than 5 mm (¼ inch)
1 onion, peeled and very thinly sliced
sea salt and freshly ground black pepper
freshly grated nutmeg
3 tablespoons filtered or spring water

Preheat the oven to 180°C/350°F/Gas Mark 4. Brush a shallow
ovenproof dish with 1 tablespoonful of the oil.

Arrange a layer of potato slices in the base of the dish, put
some of the onion rings on top and season with salt, pepper
and a grating of nutmeg. Repeat these layers, until all the
vegetables are used, ending with a layer of potato. Mix
together the water and remaining oil and pour over the top.
Finish with a final grating of nutmeg.

Cover with a piece of greaseproof paper and bake for 1
hour, removing the paper for the last half hour to brown the
top. The bake is done when you can easily push the point of
a knife through the potato.

Golden Spiced Potatoes   *Serves 4*

Serve this with a Tomato and Onion Salad (page 121) and perhaps a steamed vegetable such as French beans, or a green salad. This mixture also makes a good stuffing for tomatoes (see below).

1 onion, peeled and chopped
2 tablespoons oil
1 garlic clove, peeled and crushed
½ teaspoon ground turmeric
1 teaspoon ground coriander
1 teaspoon cumin seeds
1 kg (2 lb) potatoes, peeled and cut into 1 cm (½ inch) dice
150 ml (5 fl oz) filtered or spring water
sea salt and freshly ground black pepper
1–2 tablespoons chopped fresh coriander or parsley, if available

Fry the onion in the oil in a medium-sized saucepan for 8 minutes, then add the garlic, turmeric, coriander and cumin. Add the potatoes, turning them gently with a spoon so that they get coated with the onion and spice mixture, then add the water and some salt and pepper. Cover and leave to cook gently for about 10 minutes, or until the potatoes are just tender. Shake the pan from time to time to prevent sticking and ensure even cooking. Check the seasoning, then serve, sprinkled with chopped parsley or fresh coriander if available.

VARIATION

Tomatoes Stuffed with Golden Spiced Potatoes

Choose large, firm tomatoes, slice off the tops, scoop out the seeds, and fill with the cooked potato mixture. Stand the tomatoes in a shallow baking dish and bake in a moderate oven (180°C/350°F/Gas Mark 4) for 15–20 minutes, or until the tomatoes are heated through. Served with a lightly cooked green vegetable such as spinach, or with a crisp green salad and some brown rice if you want to make the dish more substantial.

Golden Potatoes in Coconut Cream *Serves 4*

This makes a good main course, served with Tomato and Onion Salad (page 121)and Carrot and Mustard Seed Salad (page 124), or it can be presented as one of a number of spicy dishes to serve a crowd.

225 g (8 oz) unsweetened desiccated coconut
1 litre (1¾ pints) boiling water
1 large onion, peeled and chopped
2 tablespoons olive oil
2 large tomatoes, skinned (as described on page 131) and chopped
1 green chilli, de-seeded and chopped
2 teaspoons ground turmeric
1 kg (2¼ lb) small new potatoes, scrubbed
sea salt and freshly ground black pepper
chopped fresh coriander to garnish

Put the coconut in a bowl, cover with the boiling water and leave to soak for 15–20 minutes. Meanwhile, fry the onion in the oil for 5 minutes, then add the tomatoes and chilli and fry for a further 5 minutes. Add the turmeric and stir briefly over the heat.

Strain the coconut liquid into a bowl through a sieve, squeezing out as much liquid as possible and discarding the coconut. Add the liquid to the onion mixture, together with the potatoes and some salt and pepper to taste. Simmer gently for 10–15 minutes, or until the potatoes are just tender. If there is a great deal of liquid, remove the potatoes, boil the liquid rapidly until reduced and slightly thickened, then add the potatoes again. Check seasoning. Sprinkle some chopped coriander over the top, and serve.

Baked Potatoes

Baked potatoes make one of the easiest, healthiest and most economical main courses. Simply scrub one or two large potatoes per person, prick and bake at 230°C/450°F/Gas Mark 8 for 1–1½ hours, or until the potatoes feel soft when squeezed and the skins are crisp. Then split open and serve with any of the following toppings, or simply with a few drops of rice vinegar, lemon juice or tamari, with or without a little olive oil, and plenty of freshly ground black pepper and some chopped fresh herbs or spring onions.

TOPPINGS FOR BAKED POTATOES

—Garlic Mushrooms (page 147)
—Creamy sweetcorn: heat 100 g (4 oz) frozen sweetcorn kernels, mashing some of the kernels to give a creamy consistency.
—Chilli-tomato: fry a small, finely chopped onion in 1 tablespoon olive oil until soft, then add 2 skinned and chopped tomatoes, a pinch of chilli powder, and a crushed garlic clove if you like. Stir until the mixture is heated through, then season.
—Avocado: top each baked potato with ½ ripe avocado, stoned, skinned and chopped
—Guacamole (page 117)
—Hummus (page 118)
—Japanese Dressing (page 116): a good low-calorie topping
—Tamari: also low in calories and very tasty
—Salad topping: serve with a jumbo filling of chopped tomato, cucumber, onion and shredded lettuce – or whatever is available.
—Coarsely grated carrot dressed with lemon juice or rice vinegar and a little olive oil is also good.

Bircher Potatoes   *Serves 4*

Another quick and easy potato dish which is filling and nutritious enough to make a main course. Serve with a good green salad and perhaps another salad such as grated carrot. Some Mint Sauce (page 208) goes well with these potatoes.

6 – 8 medium-sized potatoes, scrubbed
olive oil
sea salt

Set the oven to 200°C/400°F/Gas Mark 6, and brush a roasting tin generously with oil. Cut the potatoes in half lengthwise, place them (cut-side down) on the oiled tin, and sprinkle with salt. Bake the potatoes for about 45 minutes, until they are soft on top and crisp and golden brown underneath. Serve immediately.

Sliced Potatoes Baked in Olive Oil *Serves 4*

Another simple, main-course potato dish, this is delicious in the summer with fresh herbs and steamed French beans or a very fresh crunchy green salad made from small, tender, hearty lettuces.

1 kg (2 lb) potatoes, peeled
olive oil
1 – 2 garlic cloves, peeled and crushed
1 – 2 teaspoons fresh or dried herbs: thyme, rosemary and/or oregano
sea salt

Set the oven to 200°C/400°F/Gas Mark 6, and brush a large roasting tin with oil. Slice the potatoes as thinly as you can, then rinse them under cold water to remove excess starch, and pat dry on kitchen paper. Arrange the potatoes in a shallow layer on the base of the roasting tin. Brush with the oil, and sprinkle with the garlic, herbs and salt. Bake for 45 – 60 minutes, until soft inside, and golden brown and crisp round the edges.

Healthy Chips   *Serves 1*

If you make them this way, and serve them as a main course, with a good green salad and some grated carrot, you need never feel guilty about eating chips again!

350 g (12 oz) potatoes
1 tablespoon olive oil

Set the oven to 230°C/450°F/Gas Mark 8, and put a baking sheet or large roasting tin in the oven to heat up.

Meanwhile, scrub or peel the potatoes and cut into thick chunky chips. Sprinkle the oil over the chips, turning them with your hands so that they are all coated. Put the chips on the baking sheet or in the tin in a single layer.

Bake for about 20 minutes, then turn the chips, and cook for a further 20–30 minutes, turning them again if possible, until they are golden brown and crisp all over. Serve immediately.

11

Dried Bean and Lentil Dishes

How to Sprout Pulses and Grains

Many types of grain, lentil and bean (with the exception of red kidney beans and large beans such as butterbeans) are suitable for sprouting. Chick peas, alfalfa seeds, continental lentils, aduki beans, mung beans and triticale (a type of wheat) are good ones to start with. Put half a cupful of beans, grains or lentils into a jar (a big coffee jar is ideal), cover with cold filtered or spring water and leave to soak for 8 – 12 hours.

Place a piece of muslin over the top, secured with an elastic band, and tip the soaking-water out of the jar through the muslin. Fill the jar with fresh water, swish it round and then pour it all out again. All this can be done without removing the muslin, which prevents the seeds or beans falling out and blocking the sink. This rinsing has to be repeated twice a day to keep the seeds damp, but don't let them stand in water after the first soaking or they will rot.

The sprouts will soon appear, and in 2 – 4 days they will be ready to use. They can be used straight away, or kept in the fridge for several days.

As an alternative to the jar method, you can buy a sprouter, consisting of three sprouting trays which stack on top of each other, with a water-collecting bowl underneath to catch the drips after rinsing. This means you can have three different types of sprout on the go at once, or one type in several stages of development, if you're addicted!

How to Prepare and Cook Pulses

Pulses are easy to prepare, and although it's handy to keep some canned ones in the cupboard, it's cheaper and better for the environment to buy them in their dried form and cook them yourself. For all the pulses used in this book, except split red lentils and split peas, follow the steps below. (Also, note that red kidney beans need to be boiled hard for *at least* 10 minutes, to destroy any substances which can cause stomach upsets.)

1 Wash the pulses in cold water and drain.
2 Cover with their height again in cold water and soak for 6 – 8 hours, then drain and rinse. Or boil for 1 minute, cover and leave to soak for 1 hour, then drain and rinse.
3 Put the pulses in a pan with their height again in cold water, boil hard for 10 minutes, then simmer, uncovered, until tender (see 'Cooking Times for Pulses').
4 To cook in a pressure cooker, follow steps 1 and 2, then cook the pulses according to your pressure-cooking instructions (probably in a basket with a relatively small amount of water).
5 To freeze pulses, spread the cooked, drained beans out in a single layer on a tray and freeze them uncovered, then remove them from the tray, making sure the beans are separate, and put them in a large container in the freezer. I sometimes divide a 450 g (1 lb) batch into 5 portions, each one roughly equivalent to the contents of a 425 g (15 oz) can.

COOKING TIMES FOR PULSES

Type of Pulse	Cooking Time Normal	In a pressure cooker
split red lentils (don't need soaking)	20 minutes	only for liquid mixtures like soups and dal, 5 minutes
split peas (don't need soaking)	30 – 40 minutes	5 – 10 minutes
butterbeans	1¼ – 1½ hours	15 – 20 minutes
chick peas	45 minutes – 3 hours, usually about 1½ hours	10 – 40 minutes
whole green or brown lentils	45 minutes	7 – 10 minutes
Middle Eastern broad beans	1 hour	10 – 15 minutes
haricot or cannellini beans	1¼ hours	15 minutes
red kidney beans	1¼ hours	15 minutes

Green Age Chilli   *Serves 4*

Serve this chilli with brown rice, baked potatoes or whole-wheat bread for a warming main course.

2 tablespoons olive oil
2 medium onions, peeled and chopped
1 large carrot, scraped and grated
1 red or green pepper, washed, de-seeded and sliced
2 garlic cloves, peeled and crushed
1 × 425 g (15 oz) can tomatoes
½ teaspoon hot chilli powder
50 g (2 oz) mushrooms
50 g (2 oz) walnuts or pecan nuts (optional)
sea salt and freshly ground black pepper
2 × 425 g (15 oz) cans red kidney beans, or 200 g (7 oz) dried red kidney beans, soaked and cooked (as described on pages 166–7)

Heat the oil in a large saucepan, add the onion and stir. Cover and leave to cook over a moderate heat for 5 minutes, stirring occasionally. Then add the carrot and pepper and cook for a further 5 minutes.

Liquidize together (or chop very finely and mix) the garlic, tomatoes and their liquid, chilli, mushrooms and nuts, if using, and some salt and pepper. Add to the saucepan, together with the beans. Bring to a gentle simmer, then cook for about 20 minutes, stirring from time to time.

Dal   *Serves 4*

Try this with brown rice or lightly cooked cabbage, accompanied by Tomato and Coconut Salad (page 121). Dal is especially good made in advance and then reheated, because the flavours have time to develop.

200 g (7 oz) split red lentils
1 litre (1¾ pints) filtered or spring water
2 thin slices of fresh peeled ginger
½ teaspoon ground turmeric
1 tablespoon olive oil
1 teaspoon cumin seeds
1 teaspoon ground coriander
a pinch of chilli powder
1 onion, peeled and sliced
sea salt

Wash and drain the lentils, then put them in a saucepan with the water. Bring to the boil, and remove the scum. Add the ginger and turmeric to the lentils and leaver to simmer gently for 30–40 minutes, or until the lentils are very soft. Stir towards the end of the cooking time to prevent sticking.

Heat the oil in another pan and add the cumin seeds. When they start to pop, add the coriander and chilli. Stir for a moment or two, then add the onion. Cook gently for about 10 minutes, or until the onion is tender. Add this mixture to the lentils. Season to taste with salt, and serve.

Lentil Burgers   *Makes 16*

My 11-year-old daughter, Claire, helped me to make these to her taste – the potatoes and the seasonings were her idea and the result is burgers which are always popular with her and her friends. This recipe makes a lot, but they freeze well before cooking and can be cooked from frozen, allowing 10 – 15 minutes longer, or the recipe can be halved.

They are good served in baps, normal burger-style, or with chutney and cooked vegetables or salad. I like them with Multicoloured Salad (page 124).

350 g (12 oz) split red lentils
450 ml (15 fl oz) filtered or spring water
1 large onion, peeled and chopped
1 tablespoon olive oil
450 g (1 lb) potatoes, peeled and cut into even-sized pieces
1 teaspoon thyme
1 teaspoon oregano
freshly grated nutmeg
2 tablespoons chopped fresh parsley
sea salt and freshly ground black pepper
flour for coating
extra olive oil

Put the lentils in a saucepan with the water. Bring to the boil, then cover and leave to cook very gently for 20 – 25 minutes, or until the lentils are soft and pale, and all the water has been absorbed.

Set the oven to 200°C/400°F/Gas Mark 6.

Fry the onion in the oil for 10 minutes, until tender and lightly browned. Boil the potatoes until tender, then mash with with the onion. Add the lentils to the potato mixture, together with the thyme, oregano, grated nutmeg, parsley and salt and pep-per. Form the mixture into burger shapes and coat with flour.

Brush a baking sheet with olive oil and put in the oven for 5 minutes or so to heat up. Put the burgers on to the baking sheet and bake for 15–20 minutes, or until browned on one side. Then turn over and bake for a further 10–15 minutes to brown the other side.

Lentil Loaf   *Serves 4–6*

This is one of the simplest recipes for Lentil Loaf. It's good either hot or cold, with lightly cooked vegetables and a Savoury Sauce (page 207), or with a crisp salad.

500 g (1¼ lb) split red lentils
600 ml (1 pint) water
2 tablespoons olive oil
2 large onions, peeled and finely chopped
1 teaspoon mixed herbs or sage
1 tablespoon lemon juice
sea salt and freshly ground black pepper
3–4 tablespoons wholewheat flour or dried breadcrumbs to coat
extra olive oil

Put the lentils in a saucepan with the water and bring to the boil. Then turn the heat right down, cover, and cook for 20–25 minutes, or until the lentils are soft and pale-coloured and all the water has been absorbed. Keep an eye on the pan towards the end of the cooking time as the lentils may stick. However, they need to be dry, so only add a very little extra water, if any.

Meanwhile, heat the oil in a large saucepan and fry the onion for 10 minutes, covered, over a fairly gentle heat.

Set the oven to 190°C/375°F/Gas Mark 5.

Mix together the lentils, fried onions, herbs, lemon juice and some salt and pepper. Form the mixture into a loaf shape, coating it in wholewheat flour or breadcrumbs. Pour enough oil into a roasting tin to coat the base thinly and put in the oven to heat up.

When the oil is smoking hot, put the lentil loaf into the tin and spoon a little of the oil over it. Bake the loaf in the oven for about 45 minutes, or until browned and crisp all over. Spoon some of the oil over the loaf every 15 minutes or so, if possible. When crisp, lift the loaf out of the tin and on to a warmed serving dish. Serve in thick slices.

Felafel   *Serves 4*

These tasty chick pea rissoles from the Middle East are delicious with one or two salads and a dip, such as Hummus (page 118), or Guacamole (page 117). Some warm Arab bread goes well with them, too.

2 × 400 g (14 oz) cans chick peas or 200 g (7 oz) dried chick peas, prepared and cooked (as described on pages 166–7)
50 g (2 oz) onion, peeled
6 – 8 good sprigs of parsley
1 garlic clove, peeled
2 teaspoons ground coriander
sea salt and freshly ground black pepper
100 g (4 oz) dried wholewheat breadcrumbs for coating
cheapest type of olive oil for shallow-frying

Drain the chick peas, keeping the liquid on one side. If you are using a food processor, cut the onion into chunks, remove any tough stems from the parsley, combine with the chick peas and whole garlic clove and whizz to a thick purée.

If blending by hand, mash the chick peas well, grate or chop the onion very finely, crush the garlic, chop the parsley, and stir them all together.

Either way, then add the coriander and salt and pepper to taste. Divide into 8, form into rounds like golf balls, and coat thoroughly with dried breadcrumbs.

Either shallow-fry the felafel until crisp all over, and drain well; or brush them lightly with olive oil, place on a baking sheet and bake in a moderate-hot oven (180–200°C/350–400°F/Gas Mark 4–6) for 30–40 minutes, or until browned, turning them over after about 20 minutes, or when the underside is browned. Serve hot, or warm.

Spicy Beanburgers   *Makes 8*

These are easy to make and universally popular. They are good served in light burger buns, with a selection of pickles and salads which people can add themselves. They freeze well and can be cooked from frozen.

1 tablespoon olive oil
1 onion, peeled and chopped
1 carrot, scraped and finely chopped or grated
½ green pepper, washed, de-seeded and chopped
1 garlic clove, peeled and crushed
¼ – ½ teaspoon hot chilli powder (optional)
1 teaspoon ground coriander
2 × 425 g (15 oz) cans red kidney beans or 200 g (7 oz) dried red kidney beans, soaked and cooked (as described on pages 166–7)
50 g (2 oz) soft wholewheat breadcrumbs
sea salt and freshly ground black pepper
100 g (4 oz) dried wholewheat breadcrumbs for coating
a little extra olive oil

Set the oven to 200°C/400°F/Gas Mark 6.

Heat the oil in a large saucepan, add the onion and stir. Cover and leave to cook over a moderate heat for 5 minutes, stirring occasionally. Then add the carrot, pepper and garlic and cook for a further 5 minutes. Add the spices, stir for 1—2 minutes, then remove from the heat.

Mash the beans and add to the vegetable mixture with the soft breadcrumbs and salt and pepper to taste. Divide into 8, form into burgers and coat with dried breadcrumbs. Place on an oiled baking sheet and bake until brown and crisp on one side, then turn over to cook the other side. Serve hot, or warm.

Refried Red Beans   *Serves 4*

This simple dish is nice with some tortilla chips, a crisp green salad and some guacamole or slices of ripe avocado.

2 tablespoons olive oil
2 medium onions, peeled and chopped
2 garlic cloves, peeled and crushed
1 green chilli, washed, de-seeded and finely chopped
2 × 425 g (15 oz) can red kidney beans, or 200 g (7 oz) dried red kidney beans, soaked and cooked (see pages 166–7)
2 tomatoes, skinned (as described on page 131) and chopped
sea salt and freshly ground black pepper
a little fresh coriander, if available

Heat the oil in a large saucepan, add the onion and stir. Cover and leave to cook over a moderate heat for 8 minutes, stirring occasionally. Then add the garlic and chilli and cook for a further 2 minutes.

Meanwhile, drain the beans and mash roughly with a fork, to give a chunky texture. Add the beans to the onion mixture, together with the tomatoes. Cook gently, stirring, until everything is heated through. Season to taste with salt and pepper. If fresh coriander is available, snip some over the top before serving.

Middle Eastern Broad Beans

Serves 4 with side dishes

If you can get hold of some Middle Eastern broad beans, which are small round brown beans and may be called 'foul' or 'tic' beans, they make a delicious dip with a rich, earthy flavour. This is good served with some crisp Felafel (page 172) which you can dip into it, to scoop it up, and some sliced tomatoes, spring onions and lettuce, together with some lemon juice, a good fruity olive oil and some warm Arab bread. A cheap, filling and healthy meal!

225 g (8 oz) 'foul' beans
filtered or spring water
1 – 2 garlic cloves, peeled and crushed
sea salt and freshly ground black pepper
olive oil
lemon juice

Put the beans in a bowl, cover them with water and leave to soak for several hours. Or put them in a saucepan, cover with water and bring to the boil. Then remove from the heat, cover and leave to soak for 1 hour.

Simmer the beans – in fresh water, if you like – for about 1 hour, or until tender. Drain, keeping the liquid on one side, then mash or liquidize the beans with enough of their water to make the consistency you want. It will become firmer as it cools, so if you are going to serve it tepid, Middle-Eastern style, make it a bit more liquid while it is still hot. Add the garlic and some salt and pepper to taste. You can add a tablespoonful of olive oil and a squeeze of lemon juice at this stage, or you can pour them over the beans before serving.

Tofu and Tamari   *Serves 1 – 2*

This is an excellent quick savoury dish and can be eaten hot
or cold. It's very tasty and full of nutrients. Serve it with some
fresh salad – sliced tomato, lettuce or watercress.

1 packet firm tofu
1 – 2 tablespoons tamari
4 spring onions, chopped
1 – 2 pieces of nori (optional)

Drain the tofu and cut it into cubes. If you want to eat the tofu
hot, either put it under the grill until heated through, or put it
on a plate over a pan of steaming water with another plate on
top. (I think this dish as just as good cold as hot.)

Sprinkle the tamari over the tofu and mix gently until all the
pieces are coated. Then add the spring onions and mix
together. If you are using the nori, hold it near a gas flame or
electric hotplate for a few seconds, or until it is crisp all over.
Then crumble it over the top of the tofu mixture and serve
immediately.

Tofu and Mushroom Scramble   *Serves 2*

This is rather like a non-dairy version of scrambled eggs with
mushrooms. It's good on its own, or with some fingers of crisp
hot toast.

1 tablespoon olive oil
225 g (8 oz) button mushrooms, washed and sliced
1 packet silken tofu
a pinch of ground turmeric
1 tablespoon tamari
freshly ground black pepper

Heat the oil in a saucepan and fry the mushrooms for 2–3 minutes, or until just beginning to get tender. Then add the tofu, undrained, and the turmeric and tamari. Mix well over the heat, to heat through the tofu and make a scrambled texture. Season with pepper and serve immediately.

12

Rice and Other Grains

How to Prepare and Cook Grains

Grains are central to the Green Age Diet and there are many different types to choose from. Following these simple steps, you'll find them all very straightforward to cook.

1 Wash the grains under cold water until the water runs clear, then drain. For basmati rice, wash, soak in cold water for 30 minutes, then drain. Don't wash millet; toast it in a dry pan, stirring, for 2 – 3 minutes until the grains smell roasted and start to 'pop'.
2 Put the grains in a pan with the measured amount of cold water and bring to the boil. Cover, turn the heat right down and cook over the lowest possible heat for the given time.
3 Remove the saucepan from the heat but leave to stand, covered, for a further 10 – 15 minutes. Stir or 'fluff' grains gently with a fork.
4 To cook in a pressure cooker, follow steps 1 and 2, then cook the grains according to your pressure-cooker instructions. NB: Except for brown rice, I don't recommend a pressure cooker, as it's easy to overcook grains.
5 To freeze grains, divide into portions, put in containers, and place in freezer.

QUANTITIES OF WATER AND COOKING TIMES FOR GRAINS

Grain	Water per 225 g (8 oz)	Cooking Time
Brown rice	600 – 900 ml (1 – 1½ pints) the more water, the softer the texture	45 minutes
Brown basmati rice	600 ml (1 pint)	30 minutes
White long-grain rice	600 – 900 ml (1 – 1½ pints)	25 – 30 minutes
White basmati rice	600 ml (1 pint)	25 minutes
Millet	900 ml (1½ pints)	20 – 25 minutes
Pearl barley	600 – 900 ml (1 – 1½ pints)	30 minutes
Bulgur wheat (this is a pre-cooked grain, so cooking is optional)	600 ml (1 pint)	15 minutes, or just leave to soak in the water (hot or cold) for 10 – 15 minutes until the water is absorbed

Steamed Brown Rice   *Serves 4*

225 g (8 oz) long-grain brown rice
600 – 900 ml (1 – 1½ pints) filtered or spring water
½ teaspoon sea salt (optional)

Put the rice (and salt, if using) in a saucepan with the water
and bring to the boil. Then turn the heat right down, cover
and leave to cook for 40 – 45 minutes.

You can serve the rice straight away, or leave the pan on
one side with the lid still in place for a further 15 minutes, for
the rice to go on cooking in its own heat.

VARIATION

Herby Brown Rice

Make as described, mixing in 1 – 3 tablespoons chopped fresh
herbs after cooking and just before you serve the rice.

Spicy Brown Rice   *Serves 4*

This delicately flavoured golden rice is a good accompaniment
for curries, spiced vegetable mixtures and stuffed vegetables.

225 g (8 oz) brown rice
1½ tablespoons olive oil
¾ teaspoon ground turmeric
3 cloves
1 bay leaf
600 ml (1 pint) filtered or spring water
sea salt and freshly ground black pepper

Wash the rice, drain and dry on kitchen towels. Heat the oil in a medium-sized saucepan, then add the rice, and stir without browning for 3 – 4 minutes. Stir in the turmeric, cloves and bay leaf. Cook for a few seconds longer, then pour in the water and add some salt and pepper. Bring to the boil, put a lid on the saucepan and turn the heat down as low as possible. Cook for 40 – 45 minutes, until the rice is tender and all the water has been absorbed. Just before serving, fluff the rice by stirring gently with a fork.

Rice and Avocado   *Serves 4*

1 onion, peeled and sliced
2 garlic cloves, peeled and crushed
1 tablespoon olive oil
1 beefsteak tomato, skinned (as described on page 131) and chopped
1 quantity Steamed Brown Rice (page 180)
1 large ripe avocado, halved, stoned, skinned and diced
1 – 2 tablespoons lemon juice
sea salt and freshly ground black pepper
chopped fresh parsley or basil

Fry the onion and garlic in the oil for 10 minutes, then add the tomato and cook for 2 – 3 minutes, or until the tomato has heated through. Add all these ingredients to the rice, together with the avocado, lemon juice and salt and pepper to taste. Sprinkle with chopped fresh herbs and serve.

Rice with Marrow   *Serves 4*

This is very simple, but it's one of my favourite summer rice dishes. Serve with a crisp green salad.

1 onion, peeled and sliced
1 tablespoon olive oil
1 garlic clove, peeled and crushed
½ medium marrow, peeled, de-seeded and sliced
1 small green or red pepper, washed, de-seeded and chopped
225 g (8 oz) raw brown rice
225 g (8 oz) tomatoes, skinned (as described on page 131) and chopped
300 ml (10 fl oz) filtered or spring water
sea salt and freshly ground black pepper
chopped fresh parsley

Fry the onion in the oil for 5 minutes, then add the garlic, marrow and pepper, cover, and fry for a further 5 minutes. Add the rice, tomatoes and water and bring to the boil. Cover tightly, lower the heat, and leave to cook very gently for 40 – 45 minutes, or until the rice is tender and the water is absorbed. If there is still some liquid left, let the mixture stand, still covered, for 15 minutes. Season with salt and pepper, sprinkle with chopped parsley, and serve.

Mushroom Risotto *Serves 2*

This risotto is nice with chopped fresh herbs or nuts – pine nuts or whole roasted cashews – over the top. It's also good cold, as a rice salad, and makes a good stuffing for peppers (page 183). Serve with a green salad, or a few very lightly cooked fresh vegetables.

1 onion, peeled and chopped
1 tablespoon olive oil
1 garlic clove, peeled and crushed
1 large beefsteak tomato, skinned (as described on page 131)
100 g (4 oz) firm button mushrooms, washed and sliced
450 ml (15 fl oz) measure of brown rice, cooked (as described on pages 178–9)
a good squeeze of lemon juice
sea salt and freshly ground black pepper

Fry the onion in the oil in a large saucepan for 5 minutes, covered, then add the garlic, tomato and mushrooms and fry for a further 5 minutes, again covered. Add the rice and stir gently until heated through. Add a squeeze of lemon juice, and salt and pepper to taste.

Stuffed Peppers   *Serves 2*

1 quantity Mushroom Risotto (as above)
2 medium-sized green or red peppers

Set the oven to 200°C/400°F/Gas Mark 6.

Cut a small slice off the top of the peppers (including the stalks), then scoop out the seeds and rinse under the cold tap. Bring a large saucepanful of water to the boil and put in the peppers and the sliced-off tops. Simmer for 4 minutes, then drain and refresh under cold water.

Drain again, pat dry on kitchen paper, and stand in a shallow greased casserole. Spoon the rice mixture into the green peppers, replace tops, and bake for 30 minutes.

Barley Casserole   *Serves 4*

2 onions, peeled and chopped
50 g (2 oz) butter or pure vegetable margarine
1 kg (2 lb) leeks, washed, trimmed and sliced into 2.5 cm (1 inch) lengths
225 g (8 oz) carrots, scraped and diced
2 celery sticks, washed and chopped
300 g (11 oz) pearl barley
750 ml (1¼ pints) vegetable stock
sea salt and freshly ground black pepper
750 g (1½ lb) potatoes, peeled and cut into even-sized chunks
4 tablespoons chopped fresh parsley

Fry the onion in the butter or margarine for 5 minutes in a large, heavy-based saucepan. Add the leeks, carrots and celery, mixing gently, so that they get coated. Cover the pan and cook on a low heat for 5 minutes. Add the barley and mix well, then pour in the vegetable stock, with a good teaspoonful of salt and plenty of pepper. Cover and cook over a gentle heat for 40 minutes, then add the potatoes, putting them into the top of the casserole. Cook, covered, for a further 20 minutes, or until the potatoes and barley are tender and all the water has been absorbed. Check the seasoning: more salt will probably be needed. Sprinkle with the chopped parsley and serve.

Easy Millet Burgers or Sausages   *Makes 10*

These are quick and easy to make and can be flavoured in different ways; they can also be made into sausage shapes for a change.

225 g (8 oz) millet, cooked (as described on pages 178–9)
900 ml (1½ pints) filtered or spring water, boiling
2–3 tablespoons crunchy peanut butter or tahini
tamari or sea salt
freshly ground black pepper
½–1 teaspoon curry powder (optional)

Put the cooked millet in a large bowl and stir in the peanut butter or tahini, tamari or salt, and pepper to season. Add the curry powder, if using. Form the mixture into burgers or sausages, and press into shape. Shallow-fry in a little olive oil; or brush a baking sheet with olive oil, heat in the oven (set to 200°C/400°F/Gas Mark 6), then put the burgers on the baking sheet and bake for 15–20 minutes on each side, or until browned and crisp.

  Other flavourings, such as chopped parsley, crushed garlic, fried onion, fried mushrooms, chopped red or green pepper, grated fresh ginger, grated carrot or chopped spring onion, can be added to the mixture before shaping into burgers or sausages.

13

Pasta

Spaghetti with Red Pepper   *Serves 2*

225 g (8 oz) spaghetti
1 large red pepper, de-seeded and cut into eighths
1 onion, peeled and chopped
1 large garlic clove, peeled and crushed
2 tablespoons olive oil
sea salt and freshly ground black pepper
a few black olives
chopped fresh basil, if available

Cook the pasta in a large saucepan of boiling water for 8–10 minutes, or until just tender.

Meanwhile, put the pieces of pepper under a hot grill until the skin starts to get blistered and charred. Removed from the grill, cover, and let them continue to cook in their own heat. Fry the onion and garlic in the oil for 10 minutes.

Drain the pasta, return it to the saucepan, and add the onion, garlic and some salt and pepper.

Peel the outer skin off the red peppers (it should come away quite easily), then cut into strips and add to the pasta, together with the black olives and basil, if available. Serve at once.

Spaghetti with Fresh Tomato Sauce   *Serves 2*

Serve this classic dish with a crisp green salad.

1 quantity Fresh Tomato Sauce (page 210)
225 g (8 oz) spaghetti
1 tablespoon olive oil
sea salt and freshly ground black pepper

Make the sauce. Then cook the pasta in a large saucepan of boiling water for 8 – 10 minutes, or until just tender. Drain the pasta, return it to the saucepan with the oil and some salt and pepper. Then serve it out on to warmed dishes, pour over the sauce and snip a little fresh basil over the top.

Spaghetti with Pesto   *Serves 2*

Mixed Salad (page 120) or a tomato, lettuce and onion salad both go well with this.

225 g (8 oz) spaghetti
For the pesto
3 – 4 good sprigs of fresh basil, stalks removed
1 large garlic clove, peeled and crushed
50 g (2 oz) pine nuts
4 tablespoons olive oil
sea salt and freshly ground black pepper

Cook the pasta in a large saucepan of boiling water for 8 – 10 minutes, or until just tender.

Meanwhile, make the pesto. Liquidize together the basil, garlic and pine nuts until smooth, then gradually add the oil to make a thick sauce.

Drain the pasta, return it to the saucepan with the pesto and some salt and pepper and stir it with a fork to distribute the pesto. Serve at once.

Spaghetti with Avocado   *Serves 2*

This is very quick to make and is delicious with a green salad and some wholewheat garlic bread

225 g (8 oz) spaghetti
1 large garlic clove, peeled and crushed
2 tablespoons olive oil
1 large ripe avocado, halved, stoned, skinned and sliced
1 tablespoon lemon juice
1 beefsteak tomato, skinned (as described on page 131) and chopped
several sprigs of fresh basil, lightly chopped
sea salt and freshly ground black pepper

Cook the pasta in a large saucepan of boiling water for 8 – 10 minutes, or until just tender, then drain and return to the saucepan with the garlic and oil. Sprinkle the avocado with the lemon juice and add to the pasta, together with the tomato, basil, and salt and pepper to taste.

Fettucine with Creamy Mushroom Sauce

Serves 2

225 g (8 oz) fettucine
1 tablespoon olive oil
sea salt and freshly ground black pepper
For the sauce
1 tablespoon olive oil
1 small onion, peeled and chopped
1 garlic clove, peeled and crushed
225 g (8 oz) button mushrooms, washed and any larger ones halved or quartered
1 teaspoon cornflour
150 ml (5 fl oz) Soya Milk (page 109)
sea salt and freshly ground black pepper
grated nutmeg
a few sprigs of fresh parsley

Cook the fettucine in a large saucepan of boiling water for 8 – 10 minutes, or until just tender.

To make the sauce, heat the oil in a large saucepan or frying pan and fry the onion for 5 minutes. Then add the garlic and mushrooms, and fry for a further 5 minutes. Sprinkle the cornflour on top and mix in, then add the soya milk, stirring well. Stir over the heat for 1 – 2 minutes, or until the mixture has thickened slightly. Season with salt, pepper and grated nutmeg.

Drain the fettucine, return it to the saucepan with the oil and some salt and pepper. Then serve it out on to warmed dishes, pour the sauce over it and snip a little fresh parsley over the top.

14

Nut Dishes

Nut Roast   *Serves 6*

This is very moist and tasty and extremely easy to make. It's rich, so this amount is right for 6 servings, and it's as delicious cold as it is hot. It can be varied in lots of different ways, and it freezes very well.

Serve it hot with a simple salad of torn-up lettuce leaves, sliced tomato and onion, with a light dressing of olive oil and lemon juice; or with some lightly cooked carrots or French beans and new potatoes steamed or boiled in their skins. For a more elaborate meal, add a tasty gravy, apple sauce or redcurrant jelly, and perhaps roast potatoes. The next day, serve cold in slices with salad and perhaps some chutney or pickles.

1 onion, peeled and chopped
2 garlic cloves, peeled and crushed
1 tablespoon olive oil
100 g (4 oz) firm white mushrooms, washed and sliced
2 teaspoons wholewheat flour
300 ml (10 fl oz) filtered or spring water
175 g (6 oz) nuts (pecan nuts are particularly good)
5 good slices wholewheat bread, made into crumbs
1 – 2 tablespoons tamari
½ teaspoon dried rosemary

sea salt and freshly ground black pepper
extra flour, dried wholewheat breadcrumbs or sesame seeds
for coating
extra olive oil for cooking

Set the oven to 190°C/375°F/Gas Mark 5.

Fry the onion and garlic gently in the oil in a large saucepan for 5 minutes. Then add the mushrooms and fry for a further 5 minutes. Sprinkle the flour on top and stir. Next, add the water and bring to the boil, stirring. Let the mixture simmer for 2–3 minutes, and remove from the heat. Finely chop or grind the nuts in a coffee grinder or food processor. Then add the nuts, breadcrumbs, tamari and rosemary, and season with salt and pepper. The mixture should be firm enough to hold together; if not, add a few more breadcrumbs.

Form into a loaf shape and coat all over with flour, dried breadcrumbs or sesame seeds. Put about 4 tablespoons of olive oil into a roasting tin and heat for a few minutes in the oven. Put the nut loaf in the hot tin and turn it quickly so that all the sides get coated with the hot oil. Then bake for 40–45 minutes, until crisp, spooning some of the oil over the top after about 30 minutes if possible. Cut into thick slices to serve.

Nut Burgers   *Makes 8*

These are very tasty and cook excellently over a barbecue. Serve them in soft wholewheat baps or burger buns, accompanied by plenty of salad – the Mixed Salad (page 120) goes particularly well with them. They also freeze well and can be cooked from frozen.

1 onion, peeled and chopped
1 tablespoon olive oil
1 teaspoon mixed herbs
2 tablespoons wholewheat flour
200 ml (7 fl oz) filtered or spring water
225 g (8 oz) mixed nuts, some finely chopped or ground, some
coarsely chopped; some peanuts can be included
4 good slices wholewheat bread, made into crumbs
½ teaspoon yeast extract
1 tablespoon tamari (optional)
sea salt and freshly ground black pepper
flour for coating
extra olive oil for cooking

Fry the onion gently in the oil in a large saucepan for about
10 minutes, or until soft, then add the herbs and flour. Stir for
a moment over the heat, then add the water and bring to the
boil, stirring. Let the mixture simmer for 2–3 minutes, and
remove from the heat. Add the nuts, breadcrumbs, yeast
extract, and tamari, if using, then season with salt and pepper.
The mixture should be stiff enough to hold together well, but
not dry and stodgy; add a little more liquid if necessary.

Divide into 8, form into burgers and coat with flour. Either
shallow-fry the burgers until crisp all over, and drain well; or
lightly brush the burgers with olive oil, place them on a baking
sheet and bake in a moderate-hot oven (180–200°C/350–
400°F/Gas Mark 4–6) for 30–40 minutes, or until browned,
turning them over after about 20 minutes, or when the
underside is browned. Perhaps the best way of all is to cook
them on a barbecue. Serve hot, or warm.

15

Pizza and Pastry Dishes

Yeast-Dough Pizza   *Serves 4*

Yeast dough is easy to make and it's a skill well worth mastering. A good home-made pizza, thin and crisp or deep and filling, is the Green Age alternative to fatty quiches. And a Calzone (page 197), or pizza dough encasing a vegetable filling, is the alternative to a high-fat pasty. Yeast pastry can also be filled with puréed dried fruits to make Birnbrot (page 216), a healthy and delicious cake.

½ teaspoon sugar
175 ml (6 fl oz) tepid filtered or spring water
2 teaspoons dried yeast
275 g (10 oz) plain wholewheat flour, or a half-and-half mixture of wholewheat and unbleached white flour
½ teaspoon sea salt
3 tablespoons olive oil
extra olive oil
For the topping
2 large onions, peeled and chopped
1 garlic clove, peeled and crushed
2 tablespoons olive oil
100 g (4 oz) mushrooms, washed and sliced
1 red pepper, washed, de-seeded and cut into eighths

4 beefsteak tomatoes, washed and sliced
oregano or chopped fresh basil
extra olive oil
a few black olives (optional)

Dissolve the sugar in the water in a small bowl. Sprinkle in the yeast and stir, then leave on one side for 10 minutes to froth up. Put the flour, salt and oil in a bowl. Next, add the yeast mixture, mixing well with your hands to make a dough which is soft enough to knead but not sloppy. Add a tiny bit more water or flour if necessary to get this consistency.

As the dough forms you may find it easier to turn it out on to a clean work surface. Knead the dough for 5 minutes until smooth and silky. Then put the dough back in the bowl, cover with a damp cloth and leave in a warm place for about an hour (longer in a cool place) until at least doubled in size. (It's better for it to rise too much than not enough.) Punch down the dough, divide it into 4 pieces, and roll these out into circles about 10 cm (4 inches) in diameter.

Set the oven to 240°C/475°F/Gas Mark 9. Brush two large baking sheets with olive oil and put them in the oven to heat up.

To make the topping, fry the onion and garlic in the oil for 7 minutes, then add the mushrooms and fry for a further 2 – 3 minutes. Meanwhile, put the pieces of pepper under a hot grill until the skin starts to get blistered and charred. Wrap them in a cloth and leave for a few minutes to cool down and soften, then strip off the skin with a sharp knife and cut the pepper into strips.

Arrange the tomatoes, onion, mushrooms and strips of red pepper on top of the pizza circles. Sprinkle with the oregano or basil, a little olive oil and the black olives, if using.

Carefully lift the pizzas on to the sizzling hot baking sheets and quickly put them in the oven. Bake the pizzas for about 15 minutes, until puffed up and golden brown on top, and crisp underneath.

TOPPINGS FOR PIZZAS

Start with a base of sliced beefsteak tomato and fried onion rings, then add any of the following:

—Chopped basil or dried oregano
—Black olives
—Cooked asparagus spears, broccoli or spinach leaves
—Sliced mushrooms, lightly fried in olive oil
—Red, green or yellow pepper (prepared as described above)
—Baby sweetcorn (these can be put on raw)
—Strips of firm tofu, brushed with olive oil
—A sprinkling of pine nuts
—Slices of ripe avocado (add these 5 minutes before the pizzas are done, so that they just heat through)

Quick Bread Pizza   *Serves 1*

½ onion, peeled and sliced
1 garlic clove, peeled and crushed
1 tablespoon olive oil
2 thick slices wholewheat bread
1 large beefsteak tomato, washed and sliced
oregano
sea salt and freshly ground black pepper
8 black olives

Fry the onion and garlic in the oil for 10 minutes. Put the wholewheat bread on a grill pan or tin which will go under the grill. Arrange the tomato slices on the bread and top with the fried onion and garlic mixture. Sprinkle with oregano, season with salt and pepper, dot with the black olives, and grill for 4 – 5 minutes, or until the tomato has heated through. Serve at once.

Calzone   *Makes 8*

1 quantity pizza dough (page 194)
2 onions, peeled and chopped
2 tablespoons olive oil
225 g (8 oz) potatoes, peeled and cut into 5 mm (¼ inch) dice
225 g (8 oz) carrots, scraped and cut into 5 mm (¼ inch) dice
2 leeks, washed, trimmed and sliced
1 garlic clove, peeled and crushed
100 g (4 oz) mushrooms, washed and sliced
2 tomatoes, skinned (as described on page 131) and chopped
1 teaspoon oregano
sea salt and freshly ground black pepper

Make the dough and leave to rise for 1 hour, or until doubled in bulk.

Meanwhile, make the filling. Fry the onion in the oil for 5 minutes, then add the potato, carrot, leeks and garlic. Cook gently for 10 minutes, then add the mushrooms, and cook for a further 4 – 5 minutes, or until the vegetables are just tender. Add the tomatoes and oregano, and season with salt and pepper. Allow to cool.

Set the oven to 230°C/450°F/Gas Mark 8. Punch down the dough and divide into 8 pieces. Roll each piece into a circle, about 15 cm (6 inches) in diameter. Place an equal portion of filling mixture on one half of each circle of dough. Dampen the edges with cold water, fold the dough over to encase the filling, and press the edges together. Prick the calzone to allow the steam to escape, then put them on a baking sheet, cover with a clean damp cloth and leave in a warm place for 20 – 30 minutes, or until the dough is puffy. Bake the calzone for about 20 minutes, or until crisp and lightly browned.

Parsnip and Celery Strudel
with Pine Nuts   *Serves 4*

625 g (1½ lb) parsnips, scraped and diced
1 large onion, peeled and finely chopped
2 celery sticks, washed and finely chopped
2 garlic cloves, peeled and crushed
8 tablespoons olive oil
sea salt and freshly ground black pepper
4 sheets filo pastry
25 – 50 g (1 – 2 oz) pine nuts

Boil or steam the parsnips until tender. Drain and cool. Meanwhile, fry the onions, celery and garlic in 2 tablespoons of the oil, covered, for 10 minutes, or until tender. Add this mixture to the parsnips, season well with salt and pepper, and cool.

Set the oven to 200°C/400°F/Gas Mark 6 and grease a baking sheet lightly with some of the remaining oil. Lay one sheet of filo pastry out on a clean tea towel and brush with some of the olive oil. Put another piece of pastry on top and sprinkle the pine nuts over evenly. Then put another piece of filo pastry on top and brush with oil. Finally, top with the last piece and brush with oil.

Spread the parsnip mixture evenly on top, leaving a border of about 2.5 cm (1 inch) around the edges. Fold the two shorter edges down to enclose the filling, then roll up the pastry and filling like a swiss roll. Place on the baking sheet, seam-side down.

Brush with more oil and bake for 25 – 30 minutes, or until golden brown and crisp. Serve cut into thick slices, with Fresh Tomato Sauce (page 210).

Spring Rolls   *Makes 12*

Serve these with some plain boiled rice, soy sauce and some salad or Stir-Fried Chinese Vegetables (page 151).

2 onions, peeled and chopped
1 tablespoon olive oil
225 g (8 oz) button mushrooms, washed and sliced
350 g (12 oz) beansprouts
1 tablespoon tamari
sea salt and freshly ground black pepper
12 pieces filo pastry
extra olive oil for cooking

Set the oven to 200°C/400°F/Gas Mark 6.

Fry the onions in the oil for 7 minutes, until almost soft, then add the mushrooms and beansprouts and fry for a further 2–3 minutes, or until all the vegetables are cooked. Add the tamari and season with salt and pepper. Allow to cool.

Brush a baking sheet with oil. Then fold a sheet of filo pastry in half. Place a good heap of the mixture just inside one corner, fold over the corner, then the edges, and roll up, to make a neat parcel. Make the rest of the spring rolls in the same way and place them all on the baking sheet. Brush the spring rolls lightly with olive oil and bake for about 30 minutes, turning them over after about 20 minutes, so that both sides get cooked and crisp.

Basic Shortcrust Pastry

Makes 100 g (4 oz)
pastry

100 g (4 oz) plain wholewheat flour
a pinch of salt
4 tablespoons olive oil
2 tablespoons cold filtered or spring water

Put the flour in a large bowl with the salt, oil and cold water and mix to a dough. Roll out the pastry on a lightly floured board.

Samosas

Serves 4

Serve these with some mango chutney, Tomato and Onion Salad (page 121) and, for a more substantial meal, some Steamed Brown Rice (page 180) or Spicy Brown Rice (page 180). Although samosas are cooked in oil, the dough from which they're made doesn't contain as much fat as normal pastry.

For the filling
1 large onion, peeled and chopped
2 tablespoons olive oil
1 large garlic clove, peeled and crushed
1 teaspoon each: mustard seed, grated fresh ginger, ground cumin and ground coriander
750 g (1½ lb) potatoes, peeled, cooked and diced
225 g (8 oz) frozen peas, defrosted
sea salt and freshly ground black pepper
inexpensive olive oil for deep-frying

For the pastry
225 g (8 oz) plain wholewheat flour
1 teaspoon sea salt
2 teaspoons baking powder
3 tablespoons olive oil
120 – 175 ml (4 – 6 fl oz) cold filtered or spring water

First make the filling. Fry the onion in the oil for 8 minutes, until soft but not browned, then add the garlic, mustard seed, ginger, cumin and coriander, and cook for a further 2 minutes. Remove from the heat and add the potato and peas. Mix well, season with salt and pepper, then cool.

Meanwhile, make the pastry. Put the flour, salt and baking powder in a bowl, then add the oil and water. Mix to a soft but not sticky dough. Knead the dough for 5 minutes, then divide into 16 pieces. Roll each into a circle about 15 cm (6 inches) in diameter, then cut the circles in half to make 32 semi-circles. Take one of the semi-circles of pastry and brush the cut edges with water, then fold it in half and press the moistened cut edges firmly together to form a cone. Fill the cone with a heaped teaspoonful of the filling, then moisten the top edges and fold them over to enclose the filling completely. Complete the rest of the samosas in the same way.

Heat the oil until a cube of bread rises to the surface immediately and starts to turn golden brown. Then fry the samosas in batches. Drain them on kitchen paper and keep the first ones warm in the oven until they're all ready.

Vegetable Pasties   *Makes 4*

1 onion, peeled and chopped
2 tablespoons olive oil
225 g (8 oz) potatoes, peeled and cut into 5 mm (¼ inch) dice
100 g (4 oz) carrots, scraped and cut into 5 mm (¼ inch) dice
1 garlic clove, peeled and crushed
sea salt and freshly ground black pepper
2 quantities Basic Shortcrust Pastry (page 200)

First make the filling. Fry the onion in the oil for 5 minutes, then add the potato, carrot and garlic. Cook gently for 10 – 15 minutes, or until the vegetables are just tender. Season with salt and pepper. Allow to cool.

Set the oven to 200°C/400°F/Gas Mark 6. Make the pastry, divide into 4 pieces and roll each into a circle about 15 cm (6 inches) in diameter. Spoon a quarter of the potato mixture on to one half of each. Dampen the edges with cold water, fold the pastry over to encase the filling, and press the edges together. Prick the pasties a couple of times to allow the steam to escape, place them on a baking tray and bake for 20 – 25 minutes.

Onion and Fresh Herb Tofu Flan   *Serves 4*

1 quantity Shortcrust Pastry (page 200)

For the filling
2 onions, peeled and chopped
1 tablespoon olive oil
1 garlic clove, peeled and crushed
1 packet silken tofu
2 heaped teaspoons chopped fresh herbs
1 tablespoon tamari
sea salt and freshly ground black pepper
freshly grated nutmeg

Set the oven to 200°C/400°F/Gas Mark 6. Put a baking sheet in the centre of the oven, to heat up. Lightly grease a 20 cm (8 inch) flan tin. Roll out the pastry and put into the tin, trimming the edges and pricking the base. Bake for 10–15 minutes, or until set and crisp.

Meanwhile, make the filling. Fry the onion gently in the oil for 10 minutes, then liquidize half of this with the garlic and tofu. Add the fresh herbs, tamari and salt and pepper to taste. Mix in the rest of the fried onion. Spread this mixture evenly in the flan.

Turn the oven setting down to 180°C/350°F/Gas Mark 4 and bake the flan for 20–25 minutes, or until heated through and set.

VARIATIONS

Mushroom Tofu Flan

Replace one of the onions with 100 g (4 oz) button mushrooms, washed and thinly sliced. Liquidize the tofu with all the fried onion. Fry the mushrooms separately, then add to the liquidized tofu mixture.

Quick Sweetcorn Tofu Flan

Use just one onion and liquidize the tofu with this. Then add 100 g (4 oz) frozen sweetcorn kernels.

Quick Mint and Pea Tofu Flan

Use just one onion and liquidize the tofu with this. Then add 100 g (4 oz) frozen peas and 2 tablespoons finely chopped mint.

Asparagus Tofu Flan

Use just one onion and liquidize the tofu with this. Then add 225 g (8 oz) cooked fresh or frozen asparagus, cut into even-sized lengths.

Ratatouille Tofu Flan

Use a good, thick, tasty Ratatouille (page 153) instead of the onions.

Broccoli and Almond Flan

Serves 4–6 as a main course, 6–8 as a starter

1 quantity Basic Shortcrust Pastry (page 200)
750 g (1½ lb) broccoli, washed, trimmed and divided into even-sized florets
1 quantity Soya Milk Sauce (page 209)
sea salt and freshly ground black pepper
freshly grated nutmeg
25 g (1 oz) flaked almonds

Set the oven to 200°C/400°F/Gas Mark 6 and put a baking sheet in the centre of the oven, to heat up. Lightly grease a 20 cm (8 inch) flan tin. Roll out the pastry as thin as possible, and put into the tin, trimming the edges. Bake for 10–15 minutes, or until set and crisp.

Meanwhile, cook the broccoli in 2.5 cm (1 inch) boiling water for 4–5 minutes, or until just tender. Drain and mix with the sauce. Season with salt, pepper and grated nutmeg. Spoon the mixture into the flan case, sprinkle with the almonds and put back in the oven for 15–20 minutes, to heat through and brown the almonds.

VARIATIONS

Avocado Flan

Use 2 avocados instead of the broccoli. Halve, stone, skin and chop the avocados and sprinkle with the juice of a lemon. Fold the avocados into the sauce, add a crushed garlic clove, season with a good pinch of chilli powder or curry powder, or a few drops of Tabasco. Spoon the mixture into the flan case and bake for 15–20 minutes, or until the avocado is just heated through.

Mushroom Flan

Instead of the broccoli add 225 g (8 oz) sliced button mushrooms, lightly fried in 1 tablespoon of olive oil, to the sauce.

Ratatouille Flan

Use the Ratatouille mixture (page 153) as a flan filling.

16

Savoury Sauces

Savoury Sauce
Makes 450–600ml (15fl oz–1 pint)

2 tablespoons olive oil
1 onion, peeled and chopped
2 garlic cloves, peeled and crushed
4 tablespoons wholewheat flour
450–600 ml (15 fl oz–1 pint) filtered or spring water or vegetable stock
1 tablespoon tamari
sea salt and freshly ground black pepper

Heat the oil in a saucepan and fry the onion lightly for 10 minutes. Add the garlic and flour, stir for a moment or two, then stir in about 450 ml (15 fl oz) water or stock. Stir over the heat until the sauce thickens, then let it simmer gently for 10 minutes. Add the tamari, and season with salt and pepper. Reheat gently, and thin with more water or stock if necessary. Check seasoning and serve.

VARIATIONS

Wine Sauce

Replace 100 – 150 ml (3½ – 5 fl oz) water or stock with wine or cider.

Mushroom Sauce

Fry the onion for 5 minutes, add 100 g (4 oz) chopped mushrooms, then fry for a further 5 minutes, before adding the flour.

Fresh Herb Sauce

Instead of the tamari, add 1 tablespoon fresh lemon juice and 1 – 2 tablespoons chopped fresh herbs just before serving.

Mint Sauce

1 teaspoon honey
1 tablespoon boiling filtered or spring water
2 tablespoons finely chopped fresh mint
6 tablespoons rice vinegar

Dissolve the honey in the boiling water. Then add the mint and rice vinegar, and stir.

Soya Milk Sauce

*Makes 300 – 400 ml
(10 – 15 fl oz)*

Soya milk can be used instead of cow's milk to make a particularly creamy and delicious white sauce. The quantity of soya milk used depends on how thick you want the sauce – just add enough milk to give the thickness you want.

2 tablespoons olive oil
2 tablespoons flour
300 – 400 ml (10 – 15 fl oz) Soya Milk (page 108)
sea salt and freshly ground black pepper
freshly grated nutmeg

Heat the oil a little and add the flour; stir over a gentle heat for a moment or two, but don't let the flour brown. Add half the milk and stir until thickened. Then add the rest gradually, to give the thickness you want. The sauce will get thicker as it cooks, and you can always add more soya milk after cooking if necessary. Stir the sauce until smooth, then leave it on a very gentle heat for 10 minutes, to cook the flour. Add more soya milk if necessary and season to taste with salt, pepper and nutmeg.

VARIATION

Parsley Sauce

Stir 1 – 2 tablespoons chopped fresh parsley into the sauce just before serving.

209

Fresh Tomato Sauce

1 tablespoon olive oil
1 onion, peeled and chopped
1 teaspoon basil
1 large garlic clove, peeled and crushed
450 g (1 lb) fresh tomatoes, or 1 × 425 g (15 oz) can tomatoes
sea salt and freshly ground black pepper

Heat the oil in a medium saucepan and fry the onion, covered, for 5 minutes. Chop the tomatoes roughly (there's no need to skin fresh ones) and add to the onion with the basil and garlic. Mix well, then cover and simmer for 15–20 minutes. If you use fresh tomatoes, liquidize the sauce, then pour it through a sieve into a clean pan, to remove the tomato skins. If you use canned tomatoes, the sauce can be served as it is, or liquidized. Season with salt and pepper.

17

Baking

Chapattis   *Makes 12*

These circles of unleavened bread make an excellent accompaniment to curries or a Quick Lentil Soup (page 139).

250 g (9 oz) plain wholewheat flour
1½ teaspoons olive oil
1 teaspoon sea salt
about 150 ml (5 fl oz) cold filtered or spring water

Put the flour in a bowl with the oil, salt and water, and mix to a soft dough. Turn the dough out on to a floured surface and knead for 5 minutes. Cover the dough with a damp cloth and leave for 2 – 3 hours, then knead again for a few minutes and divide into 12 pieces. Form each one into a ball, then roll them out with a rolling pin so that they are about 15 – 20 cm (6 – 8 inches) in diameter.

   Fry the chapattis on both sides in an ungreased frying pan until lightly flecked with brown. Pile them up on a plate as they're done, covering with a piece of foil to prevent them drying out. The chapattis can be brushed over with a little olive oil before serving, if you like.

The Grant Loaf
Makes 2 × 450 g (1 lb) loaves

This is a moist loaf, full of little holes and with a nice, heavy texture. It's the easiest bread of all to make.

olive oil
2 teaspoons dried or easy-blend yeast
350 ml (12 fl oz) tepid filtered or spring water
1 teaspoon brown sugar
450 g (1 lb) 100 per cent wholewheat flour
2 teaspoons sea salt
extra wholewheat flour

Thoroughly grease two 450 g (1 lb) loaf tins with olive oil. If you're using ordinary dried yeast, put it in a small jug with half the water and half the sugar. Stir, then leave for 10 minutes until it's frothed up like a glass of beer. (If it doesn't froth up, either the yeast was stale, or the water was too hot and has killed it. Throw it away and start again, making sure the yeast is fresh.)

Whichever kind of yeast you're using, put the flour in a bowl with the remaining sugar (or the whole teaspoonful, if you're using easy-blend yeast) and the salt. Stir in the easy-blend yeast, if using, and all the tepid water. If you're using dried yeast, add the frothed-up mixture to the flour, together with the remaining tepid water. Mix to a soft consistency (just too wet to knead), then divide the dough between the 2 tins. Cover with a damp cloth and leave to rise in a warm place for about 30 minutes.

Meanwhile, preheat the oven to 200°C/400°F/Gas Mark 6. When the dough has risen to within 5 mm (¼ inch) of the tops of the tins, put them in the oven and bake for 30 minutes. Turn the loaves out on to a wire rack to cool.

Oatcakes   *Makes 16*

These thin, crisp oatcakes are good with a dip or can be spread with honey or no-added-sugar jam for a sweet snack.

120 ml (4 fl oz) boiling filtered or spring water
½ teaspoon sea salt
1 teaspoon olive oil
150 g (5 oz) medium oatmeal

Set the oven to 180°C/350°F/Gas Mark 4.

Measure the boiling water into a jug and stir in the salt and oil. Put the oatmeal in a bowl and add the water mixture. Mix well, then leave for 2–3 minutes for the oatmeal to swell. Turn the oat mixture on to a floured board, knead lightly and divide into 2 pieces. Roll each piece into a circle, then cut each circle across into 8 wedge-shaped pieces. Roll each piece as thinly as possible, rolling from cut edge to cut edge (not from the outer edge to the point) to make a good wedge shape.

Put the oatcakes on a baking sheet and bake for 20–25 minutes, turning over halfway through. They should be pale golden, crisp and curled at the edges. Cool on a wire rack.

Quick Wholewheat Rolls — *Makes 8–10 rolls*

These light home-made rolls are quick to make. You can use all wholewheat flour, but half-and-half wholewheat and unbleached white flour gives a lighter result. The fruity variation makes a nice low-fat, low-sugar snack that is also sweet; or for a treat I sometimes put some glacé icing on the plain buns. Not 100 per cent Green Age, I know, but children love them and they're much healthier than high-fat, high-sugar cakes and sweets.

1 teaspoon brown sugar
300 ml (10 fl oz) tepid filtered or spring water
1 tablespoon dried yeast or 1 packet easy-blend yeast
225 g (8 oz) wholewheat flour
225 g (8 oz) unbleached white flour
1 teaspoon sea salt
4 tablespoons light-tasting olive oil

If using ordinary dried yeast dissolve the sugar in the water in a small bowl, sprinkle in the yeast, then leave on one side for 10 minutes to froth up. (If it doesn't froth up, either the yeast was stale, or the water was too hot, and has killed it. Throw it away and start again, making sure the yeast is fresh.) Put the flour, salt and oil in a bowl. Then add the easy-blend yeast or the yeast mixture, mixing well with your hands to make a dough which is soft enough to knead but not sloppy. Add a tiny bit more water or flour if necessary to get this consistency.

As the dough forms you may find it easier to turn it out on to a clean work surface. Knead the dough for 5 minutes until smooth and silky. Then put the dough back into the bowl, cover with a damp cloth and leave in a warm place for about an hour (longer in a cool place) until at least doubled in size. (It's better for it to rise too much than not enough.) Set the oven to 220°C/425°F/Gas Mark 7.

Punch down the dough, then knead it again for 1–2 minutes. Shape into 12 rolls, and place well apart on a floured baking tray. Cover loosely with a clean damp cloth and leave in a warm place for 15–20 minutes, or until well risen. Bake for 15–20 minutes. Cool on a wire rack and serve warm.

VARIATIONS

Fruit Buns

Make the dough as described. After the first rising, punch down the dough, then knead into it ½ teaspoon each mixed spice, cinnamon and grated nutmeg; 75 g (3 oz) currants, 50 g (2 oz) chopped mixed peel and 25 g (1 oz) brown sugar. Form into 12 rolls and continue as above.

Iced Buns

Make the rolls as described. When they are cool, cover the tops with a glacé icing made by mixing together 175 g (6 oz) icing sugar with a little water to make a thick consistency.

Birnbrot   *Serves 8–10*

This is pleasant served with coffee, or, warm from the oven, as a pudding.

1 quantity pizza dough (page 194)

For the filling
300 ml (10 fl oz) filtered or spring water
100 g (4 oz) pitted prunes
225 g (8 oz) dried pears
50 g (2 oz) raisins
rind and juice of ½ lemon
¼ teaspoon ground cinnamon
grated nutmeg
2 tablespoons kirsch (optional)

Make the dough as described. While it is rising to double its size, make the filling. Put the water and dried fruit in a pan and simmer gently until the fruit is soft, thick and dry. Finely chop or liquidize the mixture, then add the lemon rind and juice, cinnamon, a good grating of nutmeg and the kirsch, if using.

Knead the risen dough briefly, then roll it out on a floured surface to make a large square of about 38 cm (15 inches) on each side. Spread the fruit mixture over the square to within 2.5 cm (1 inch) of the edges. Fold the edges over to enclose the filling, then roll up firmly like a swiss roll. Place the roll on a baking tray which has been lightly brushed with olive oil.

Prick the birnbrot all over, cover loosely with a clean, damp cloth and put into a warm place for 20–30 minutes to rise. Set the oven to 180°C/350°F/Gas Mark 4. When risen, bake for 35 minutes, or until golden brown and crisp. Cool on a wire rack.

This is nice, especially at Christmas, with a filling of mincemeat, or try the variation below.

VARIATION

Almond Slice

This delicious variation can either be made with 2 packets of bought marzipan, or, for a healthier but more costly version, with marzipan made by mixing together 225 g (8 oz) ground almonds, 225 g (8 oz) brown sugar and enough lemon juice to bind. Roll out the dough as described, then roll out the marzipan to cover the dough to within 1 cm (½ inch) of the edges. Roll up as described, cover loosely with a clean damp cloth and put into a warm place for 20–30 minutes to rise, then bake. Serve as it is, or brush with some melted apricot jam, or drizzle a little glacé icing on top and scatter with a few flaked almonds.

Melba Toast   *Serves 4*

This thin, crisp toast goes well with many dips. It can be made a few hours in advance and kept in an airtight tin until needed. I generally use pieces of bread from a sliced loaf because these are easier to slit in half.

6 – 8 slices wholewheat bread from a sliced loaf

Toast the bread on both sides as usual, then with a sharp knife cut through the bread to split each piece in half, making each into two thin pieces. Place these pieces, untoasted side up, on a grill pan and grill until crisp and browned – the edges will curl up. Cool on a wire rack.

Fruit Cake   *Makes a 20 cm (8 inch) round cake*

This is a delicious fruit cake, made without any dairy produce.

350 g (12 oz) plain wholewheat flour
2 teaspoons mixed spice
225 g (8 oz) mixed dried fruit
125 g (4 oz) glacé cherries, halved
175 g (6 oz) Barbados sugar
200 ml (7 fl oz) light olive oil
juice and grated rind of 1 well-scrubbed orange
150 ml (5 fl oz) tepid water
¼ teaspoon bicarbonate of soda
2 tablespoons vinegar, any type
50 g (2 oz) flaked almonds

Set the oven to 150°C/300°F/Gas Mark 2. Grease a 20 cm (8 inch) cake tin and line with a double layer of greased greaseproof paper.

Sift the flour and spice into a bowl, adding the bran from the sieve, too, if you're using 100 per cent wholewheat flour. Add the dried fruit, cherries, sugar, oil and orange juice and rind. Put the water into a small bowl or jug and add the bicarbonate of soda and vinegar. Immediately add this to the cake mixture. Mix well, then spoon into the tin and level the top. Sprinkle with the almonds.

Bake for 2–2½ hours, or until a skewer inserted into the centre of the cake comes out clean. Leave the cake in the tin to cool, then strip off the greaseproof paper.

Chocolate Sponge Cake

Makes a 20 – 22 cm (8 – 8½ inch) round cake

This recipe makes an excellent light sponge cake, very similar in texture to one made with eggs. You could use carob instead of chocolate if you prefer.

225 g (8 oz) self-raising 85 per cent wholewheat flour
50 g (2 oz) cocoa powder
50 g (2 oz) soya flour
1 teaspoon bicarbonate of soda
225 g (8 oz) brown sugar
200 ml (7 fl oz) light olive oil
150 ml (5 fl oz) orange juice
150 ml (5 fl oz) filtered or spring water
1½ teaspoons vanilla essence

For the filling, icing and decoration
225 g (8 oz) plain chocolate (made without any dairy produce)
4 tablespoons Soya Milk (page 109)
a little coarsely grated chocolate

Set the oven to 180°C/350°F/Gas Mark 4. Grease two 20 – 22 cm (8 – 8½ inch) loaf tins and line each one with a circle of greased greaseproof paper.

Sift the flour, cocoa, soya flour and bicarbonate of soda into a bowl, then add the sugar. Mix the oil, orange juice, water and vanilla essence, then add to the dry ingredients and mix to a smooth, fairly wet batter. Pour the batter into the tins. Bake for 40 minutes, or until the cakes spring back to a light touch in the centre. Turn on to a wire rack and remove the paper. Allow to cool.

To make the filling and icing, break the chocolate into pieces and melt in a bowl set over a pan of gently steaming water. Gradually stir in the soya milk. Sandwich the cakes together with half the chocolate mixture and use the rest to coat the top. Decorate with grated chocolate.

Parkin   *Makes 12 – 16 slices*

A dark, sticky parkin that is always very popular.

100 g (4 oz) plain 100 per cent wholewheat flour
2 teaspoons baking powder
2 teaspoons ground ginger
100 g (4 oz) medium oatmeal
3 rounded tablespoons real Barbados sugar
100 g (4 oz) black treacle
100 g (4 oz) golden syrup or honey
120 ml (4 fl oz) light olive oil
175 ml (6 fl oz) Soya Milk (page 109)

Set the oven to 180°C/350°F/Gas Mark 4 and line a 20 cm (8 inch) square tin with greased greaseproof paper. Sift the flour, baking powder and ginger into a bowl, adding the residue of bran from the sieve, and also the oatmeal. Put the sugar, treacle, syrup or honey and oil in a saucepan and heat gently. Cool until you can comfortably put your hand against the pan, then add the soya milk. Add the treacle mixture to the dry ingredients, mixing well, then pour the mixture into the prepared tin. Bake for 50 – 60 minutes, or until firm to the touch. Lift the parkin out of the tin and put on a wire tray to cool, then cut into pieces and strip off the paper.

18

Puddings

Peach Ice   *Serves 4*

This is delicious. The peaches are frozen beforehand and the
ice needs to be made just before you want to eat it but only
takes a few moments to do.

4 medium-sized peaches
1 packet silken tofu, drained
2 teaspoons vanilla essence
1 – 2 tablespoons maple syrup (optional)

Wash the peaches and cut them into small chunks, discarding
the stones. Put the chunks in the freezer for several hours, until
solid. Just before you want to serve the ice, put the tofu in a
food processor with the frozen peach pieces and the vanilla
essence and whizz to a thick, frozen purée. Add some maple
syrup if you want to make the mixture sweeter – though I don't
think it needs this myself.

To serve, you can drizzle a little maple syrup over the top,
or decorate with some strawberries or raspberries. Alternatively, you could make a smooth sauce by whizzing raspberries
with a little maple syrup, then sieving, and pouring over the
ice.

VARIATIONS

Many different soft fruits can be used for this ice.

Mango Ice

This is particularly good: use 1 large mango, peeled and stoned, instead of the peaches.

Orange Ice

Use 2 large juicy oranges (with peel and pips removed) instead of the peaches.

Apricot Ice

Use 6 – 8 apricots, washed and stoned, instead of the peaches.

Strawberry Ice

Use 225 g (8 oz) strawberries, hulled, washed and frozen, instead of the peaches.

Pear and Honey Sorbet   *Serves 4*

4 William pears or Cox apples
100 g (4 oz) raw organic honey
filtered or spring water
juice of 1 lemon

Peel, core and quarter the pears or apples. Put in a saucepan with the honey and enough water to just cover. Poach gently for 10–15 minutes, or until tender. Remove the pears or apples and boil the liquid until thick and syrupy – it should feel tacky when tested between finger and thumb. Purée the pears or apples, and the syrup, with the lemon juice. Cool, then freeze.

If you have a food processor, let the mixture freeze completely, then cut into chunks, process until thick and light and serve immediately, or return to the freezer. If making the sorbet by hand, freeze the mixture until half-solid, then remove from the freezer and whisk hard until thick and light. Return to the freezer until firm.

To serve, remove the sorbet from the freezer 30 minutes or so beforehand, and process or whisk again before serving.

Mango Sorbet   *Serves 4*

2 mangos, peeled, stoned and cut into chunks
300 ml (10 fl oz) filtered or spring water
a little raw organic honey

Purée the mango and water until smooth, and add a little honey to sweeten. Pour into a shallow container and freeze.

If you have a food processor, let the mixture freeze completely, then cut into chunks, process until thick and light and serve immediately, or return to the freezer. If making the sorbet by hand, freeze the mixture until half-solid, then remove from the freezer and whisk hard until thick and light. Return to the freezer until firm.

To serve, remove the sorbet from the freezer 30 minutes or so beforehand, and process or whisk again before serving.

Banana Cream   *Serves 2*

This is smooth and creamy, rather like the consistency of thick yogurt. Other fruits can be used instead of the banana, or can be chopped and added to the banana cream before serving, to give an interesting texture.

2 bananas, peeled and cut into chunks, then frozen until firm
1 packet silken tofu, drained
2 fresh strawberries, grapes or a few chopped nuts to decorate
a few drops vanilla essence

Put the banana in the liquidizer with the tofu and whizz until thick and smooth. Serve in individual glasses decorated with a fresh strawberry, a grape or a few chopped nuts.

Strawberry Cream   *Serves 4*

225 g (8 oz) strawberries, hulled and washed
225 g (8 oz) silken tofu, drained
1 – 2 tablespoons raw organic honey
a few flaked almonds

Remove 2 small strawberries for decoration. Put the rest of the strawberries in the liquidizer or food processor with the tofu and honey, and whizz until thick and smooth. Add a little more honey if necessary. Pour into 4 individual dishes. Halve the reserved strawberries, put one half on top of each portion, and sprinkle with the flaked almonds.

Peaches in White Wine   *Serves 4*

4 large ripe peaches
2 tablespoons maple syrup, raw organic honey or sugar
120 ml (4 fl oz) sweet white wine

Skin the peaches by covering them with boiling water, leaving for 2 – 3 minutes, then slipping the skins off with a sharp knife. Slice the peaches, discarding the stones. Put the peach slices in a bowl, add the syrup, honey or sugar, then the wine. Mix gently. Chill before serving.

Pears in Red Wine   *Serves 4*

4 firm dessert pears
4 tablespoons maple syrup, raw organic honey or brown sugar
300 ml (10 fl oz) red wine
300 ml (10 fl oz) filtered or spring water

Peel the pears, leaving them whole and with the stalks still intact. Put the syrup, honey or sugar in a saucepan with the wine and water, and bring slowly to the boil. Add the pears, then cover and simmer for 40 minutes, or until the pears are tender right through to the centres. Remove from the pan, then boil the liquid hard until it has reduced by half. Pour this over the pears. Cool, then chill.

Baked Apples   *Serves 4*

4 large cooking apples
100 g (4 oz) raisins or dates

Set the oven to 180°C/350°F/Gas Mark 4. Wash the apples and remove the cores, leaving a neat cavity. Fill this cavity with the raisins or dates. Score round the middle of each apple, then place them in a baking dish. Bake for about 30 minutes, or until the apples are tender.

Banana and Almond Crumble   *Serves 4*

This is an unusual crumble but one that I am fond of because it relies mainly on the natural sweetness of the bananas, with very little added sugar.

4 large bananas
100 g (4 oz) wholewheat flour
50 g (2 oz) ground almonds
2 tablespoons light olive oil
50 g (2 oz) soft brown sugar
25 g (1 oz) flaked almonds

Set the oven to 190°C/375°F/Gas Mark 5. Peel and slice the bananas and arrange them in a shallow ovenproof dish. Mix together the flour, ground almonds and olive oil, to make a crumble mixture, then add the sugar and flaked almonds. Spread this mixture evenly over the top of the bananas. Bake for about 20 minutes, or until the crumble is golden brown.

CHIEF SEATTLE'S TESTIMONY

I would like to leave you with this prophetic speech which was
made in 1854, by the great Indian Chief, Seattle, when he was
faced with the loss of his tribe's land.

We are part of the earth and it is part of us.
The perfumed flowers are our sisters;
the deer, the horse, the great eagle,
these are our brothers.
The rocky crests, the juices of the meadows,
the body heat of the pony, and man —
all belong to the same family.

So, when the Great Chief in Washington sends word
that he wishes to buy our land, he asks much of us ...

If we decide to accept, I will make one condition:
The white man must treat the beasts of this land
as his brothers.
I am a savage and do not understand any other way.
I have seen a thousand rotting buffalos on the prairie,
left by the white man who shot them from a passing train.
I am a savage and I do not understand how the smoking
iron horse can be more important than the buffalo
that we kill only to stay alive.

Where is man without the beasts?
If the beasts were gone, men would die
from a great loneliness of spirit.
For whatever happens to the beasts
soon happens to man.

All things are connected.
This we know.
The earth does not belong to man.
Man belongs to the earth.
This we know.
All things are connected
like the blood which unites one family.
All things are connected.
Whatever befalls the earth befalls the sons of the earth.
Man did not weave the web of life,
he is merely a strand in it.
Whatever he does to the web,
he does to himself.

From Jan Wynne-Tyson (ed.), *The Extended Circle*, Centaur Press, 1985.

USEFUL ADDRESSES

THE ARK, 498–500 Harrow Road, London W9 3QA, tel: 01 968 6780

CHICKENS LIB, PO Box 2, Holmfirth, Huddersfield, HD7 1QT

CLEARSPRING NATURAL GROCER, 196 Old Street, London EC1, tel: 01 250 1708

COMPASSION IN WORLD FARMING, 20 Lavant Street, Petersfield, Hampshire GU32 3EW, tel: 0730 64208

FOOD ADDITIVES CAMPAIGN TEAM (FACT), Room W, 25 Horsell Road, London N5 1XL (send an SAE for information)

FRIENDS OF THE EARTH, 26–28 Underwood Street, London N1 7JQ, tel: 01 490 1555

GREEN FARM NUTRITION CENTRE, Burwash Common, East Sussex TN19 7LX, tel: 0435 882482 (for information about water filters)

GREENPEACE, 30–31 Islington Green, London N1 8BR, tel: 01 354 5100

HENRY DOUBLEDAY RESEARCH ASSOCIATION, Ryton-on-Dunsmore, Coventry, Warwickshire CV8 3LG, tel: 0203 303517

THE LAND AND FOOD COMPANY, Leggatts Park, Potters Bar, Hertfordshire EN6 1NZ, tel: 0707 58561 or 0453 860844

MARIGOLD HEALTHFOODS LTD, Unit 10, St Pancras Commercial Centre, 63 Pratt Street, London NW1 0BY

THE ORGANIC GROWERS ASSOCIATION, Aeron Park, Llangeitho, Near Tregaron, Dyfed, Wales

OXFAM, 272 Banbury Road, Oxford OX2 7DZ, tel: 0865 56777

PERFECT GLASS SHOP, 5 Park Walk, London SW10

PMT ADVISORY SERVICE, *see* Women's Nutritional Advisory Service

THE SOIL ASSOCIATION, 86 Colston Street, Bristol BS1 5BB, tel: 0272 290661

TRAIDCRAFT PLC, Mail Order Department, Kingsway, Gateshead NE11 0NE (send for a catalogue showing their wide range of products from the Third World)

THE VEGAN SOCIETY, 33–35 George Street, Oxford OX1 2AY, tel: 0865 722166

THE VEGETARIAN SOCIETY, Parkdale, Dunham Road, Altrincham, Cheshire, tel: 061 928 0793

VINTAGE ROOTS, 25 Manchester Road, Reading, Berks RG1 3QE

WOMEN'S NUTRITIONAL ADVISORY SERVICE (incorporating the Pre-menstrual Tension Advisory Service), PO Box 268, Hove, E. Sussex, BN3 1RW, tel: 0273 771366

BIBLIOGRAPHY

Magazines and Periodicals

The Environment Digest, Subscriptions Office, Worthyvale, Manor Farm, Camelford, Cornwall PL32 9TT (for information on international developments in relation to ecology)

Food First News, Institute for Food and Development Policy, 1885 Mission Street, San Francisco, CA 94103-3584, USA (publications available in the UK from Third World Publications, 151 Stratford Street, Birmingham B11 1AG, tel: 021 773 6572)

The Food Magazine, The London Food Commission, 88 Old Street, London EC1V 9AR

The Good Wood Guide, obtainable from Friends of the Earth.

Here's Health Magazine, Argus Publications, available at newsagents and healthfood shops

The Living Earth, The Soil Association

The Vegetarian, ESG Publishing Ltd, available at newsagents

Books

Birkin, Michael, and Price, Brian, *C for Chemicals, Chemical Hazards and How to Avoid Them*, Green Imprint, 1989

Christensen, Karen, *Home Ecology*, Arlington Books, 1989

Diamond, Harvey and Marilyn, *Fit For Life*, Warner Books, 1985

Elkington, John, and Hailes, Julia, *The Green Consumer Guide*, Gollancz, 1988

Elliot, Rose, *Your Very Good Health*, Fontana, 1985, *Rose Elliot's Mother and Baby Book*, Fontana, 1989

Gold, Mark, *Living Without Cruelty*, Green Imprint, 1988

Grigson, Jane, *Book of Fruit*, Penguin, 1983

Hausman, P., *Jack Sprat's Legacy – The Science and Politics of Fat and Cholesterol*, Richard Mauk Publishers, New York, 1981

Howlett, Lis, *The Cruelty-Free Shopper*, Bloomsbury, 1989

Kenton, Leslie, *The Biogenic Diet*, Arrow Books, 1986

Kenton, Leslie and Susannah, *Raw Energy*, Century, 1984

Klaper, Dr Michael, *Pregnancy, Children and the Vegan Diet* and *Vegan Nutrition: Pure and Simple*, Dr Michael Klaper, PO Box 959, Felton, CA 95018-0959, USA

Lappe, Frances Moore, *Diet for a Small Planet*, tenth anniversary edition, Ballantine Books, New York, 1981

McConnell, Carol and Malcolm, *The Mediterranean Diet*, The Bodley Head, 1987

McDougall, John, *McDougall's Medicine*, New Century Publishers, USA, 1985

Moscovitz, Judy, *The Rice Diet Report*, Bantam, New York, 1988

Polunin, Miriam, *The Right Way to Eat*, Dent, 1984

Rippon, Sadhya, *The Bristol Recipe Book*, Century, 1987

Robbins, John, *Diet for a New America*, Stillpoint Publishing, Box 640, Walpole, NH 03608, USA

Schell, O., *Modern Meat*, Vintage Books, Random House, New York, 1985

Seymour, John, and Girardet, Herbert, *Blueprint for a Green Planet*, Dorling Kindersley, 1989

Verrett, J., and Carper, J., *Eating May Be Hazardous to Your Health*, Simon and Schuster, New York, 1974

Walsh, J., *The Meat Machine*, Columbus Books, USA, 1986

Index of Subjects

Index of Recipes

239